LEGENDS OF HIAWATHA, VISIONS OF DEGANAWIDAH, and other STORIES I LOVE TO TELL

by John Franklin Phillips

Published by American Indian Books, John Franklin Phillips
317 Orchid Lane, Birmingham, Alabama 35215

Printed by Craftsman Printing Inc., Birmingham, Alabama

Library of Congress catalogue number:
ISBN number . . . 0-9618289-5-1 paperback
0-9618289-6-x hardback

Other books by the author:
The Indian Heritage of Americans, c — 1981
The American Indian in Alabama and the Southeast, c — 1984
Chief Junaluska of the Cherokee Indian Nation, c — 1986

To dear Friends, Ralph & Mary Ann

John Franklin Phillips
& Frances 12-23-2001

SPECIAL ACKNOWLEDGEMENTS

Grateful acknowledgement to Dorothy Carter McDonald for the beautiful picture of Hiawatha in his White, Birch-bark Canoe that she did for the cover of this book.

I am grateful for the help of my family in this endeavor, especially for the help of Jason for doing the artwork and illustrations for the Stories, and for Jason and Lauren in the preparation of the text, and records.

A special 'Thank You!' to Jim Pate, of The Birmingham Public Library, Tutwiler Collection of Southern History and Literature for his help in this endeavor.

Contents

SECTION ONE: NATIVE AMERICAN HERITAGE STORIES

Contents (continued)

SECTION TWO: STORIES FOR CHILDREN

Contents (continued)

Irving Powless, Jr.
Onondaga Nation
Box 319 B Hemlock Road
Nedrow, New York 13120

May 1, 2000

John F. Phillips
317 Orchid Lane
Birmingham, Al. 35215

Greetings:

First, you will see that the scholars that you quote do not agree with the date of the starting of the Haudenosaunee. We have our own starting date and it is around 1140 AD.
Second, When we formed the Haudenosaune we did not form the Iroquois Confederacy. The name Iroquois came to us after the French people arrived in what is now Canada and the United States therefore we could not have formed the "Iroquois Confederacy."
Third, we were not tribes. We are nations of people. Were is past tense. We are still here today operating under the law of the Haudenosaunee as set forth so many years ago.
Fourth, the leaders were not elected, our leaders were not known as "Sachems." This definition came after the Europeans arrived and gave our leaders names that they understood such as "Chiefs" or "Sachems."
Fifth, only the Onondaga Nation has the power to convene a General Council of the Haudenosaunee.

These are a few of the errors. If you look at their statements you can see the contradictions of the scholars of that time. Good luck in your humble endeavor and we thank you for the time spent in telling the world about the achievements of the Haudenosaunee. There are many and your publications will inform the public of some of them.

Dawnaytoh,

Chief Irving Powless, Jr.
Onondaga Nation of the
Haudenosaunee Nations

(Excerpts from a letter of Chief Irving Powless, Jr., who edited my work relating to the Haudenosaunee.)

INTRODUCTION OF THE AUTHOR

You are going to enjoy reading "THE STORIES I LOVE TO TELL" by Reverend John Franklin Phillips. It will be interesting, informative, and inspiring as you stroll with Franklin into childhood memories and his life long experience of Christian ministry and of American Indian associations, studies, lecturing, and service.

Franklin, a United Methodist clergyman, retired in the North Alabama Conference, began his passionate search for knowledge about Native Americans of the Southeast and the nation, in 1966, when Dr. Herscher of the University of Georgia, insisted he take a mini-course on archeology with him, at the "Burnt Indian Village", on the banks of the Chattahoochee River. Since then, this man has shared his stories and artifacts related to American Indian history and culture to some 250 classes from elementary schools to universities. He has also written three other books on The American Indian: (1) THE INDIAN HERITAGE OF AMERICANS, 1981, (2) THE AMERICAN INDIAN IN ALABAMA AND THE SOUTHEAST, 1984, and (3) CHIEF JUNALUSKA OF THE CHEROKEE INDIAN NATION, 1986. All his works have been written to raise the level of awareness of Native American contributions to this nation and the church, and to increase appreciation for American Indian history, traditions, culture, and spirituality.

This leader-scholar-servant, Franklin Phillips, has not only told us of unjustices perpetrated against American Indians and African Americans, but has demonstrated courageous ministry commitment to justice, human rights, equal opportunities, and inclusive community. I will always be grateful for his friendship, partnership, partnership and contribution to Native American ministry in the Southeast.

Robert Lee Mangum, A.B., B.D., L.H.D.
Retired, Former Executive Director (1991-1999)
Southeastern Jurisdictional Agency for Native American
Ministries of the United Methodist Church (SEJANAM)

INTRODUCTION

In 1976, the year of the great Celebration - the year of The 200th, Year Celebration of the birth of The United States of America - my wife, Frances, and I were serving in The Chattahoochee valley , where I was Pastor of The Langdale United Methodist Church.

Rightly so, there were many Great Celebrations, all across this great and wonderful land - America - about that marvelous achievement. And many of the leaders of The Thirteen Colonies were remembered , and praised for their achievements, and the risks they were willing to make to be free and independent.

During this time of Celebration, I remembered an experience with Dr. Herscher, of the University of Georgia excavation of 'Burnt Indian Village'. I was much impacted by his statement to me, that in The Village Council house these primitive Creek Indian People had practiced the purest form of democracy on earth!

The Native Americans were not receiving much attention or credit, in the local, or area Celebrations. But, even more troubling to me, they were not receiving much credit for such signal achievements, as developing democracy, in The National Celebrations.

I found myself, very much impacted by Dr. Herscher's comment, and making effort, from time to time, to find sources from which I might learn the truth about their achievements. This led to research about The Iroquois League or Confederacy, where I became convinced that they had , in fact, been the major root, along with the achievements in self-determination of The Athens City-State experiment, The Magna Carta, The Mayflower Compact, and The British Parliament of The Birth of Democracy of The United States of America.

During the same time frame, I had a visitor, to my office at the church, from Auburn University and The State of Alabama, who challenged me to be a volunteer for the schools of Alabama, to share my Indian Artifact Display, and Stories with the students. Since that time, I have shared my Display and spoken of American Indian History and achievements, with some 250 classes of kindergarten, elementary, middle, high school, college, and university.

These two influences led to the inspiration to write this book - STORIES I LOVE TO TELL.

And through that blessed word of Isaiah, I found myself singing - "They that wait upon The lord, shall renew their strength......."

Isaiah 40:31

They who wait for the Lord
shall renew their strength,
They shall mount up
with wings like eagles,
They shall run and not be weary,
They shall walk
and not faint.

Picture of Yosemite National Park and Valley - an Eagle looking area.
Calligraphy of Isaiah 40:31, done by Marguerite Busby.

With Wings of Eagles

With wings of Eagles,
Go my dear children and
Wait in The Spirit, for your Vision,
In quiet and humble patience,
Seek for The Wisdom of The Ages!
And in confident perseverance you will
Find the Strength to rise up with confidence
And climb Life's Mountains,
To walk the long and rugged Trails,
And to Soar through the turblence
and storms,
To meet triumphantly each and all
of life's challenges!
And at last, to find Inner Peace,
and The Crown of Life!

Inspired by:
Isaiah 40:31

Calligraphy-With Wings of Eagles, done by Margurite Busby.

A beautiful setting in which John Michael loved to walk

IN MEMORIAM

July 19, 1951 — October 2, 1998

In the great sorrow and loss of our dear Son, John Michael Phillips, October 2nd, 1998, his Mother joins with me in Dedicating this Book: AS A MEMORIAL TO MIKE

The Gardendale-Mount Vernon United Methodist Church where John Michael and LuAnn began their lives together, were youth leaders, and where his untimely Funeral Services were conducted.

WE LOVE YOU MICHAEL

Would that we could touch your hearts and help.
Would that we could do better than love, but then,
What more is there to give than
LOVE?
Wouldn't it be nice if life came with a script
We could read it at our leisure and make changes.
We could mold it for our very own
And return over and over and remember and be happy.

We could frame that smile, breathe that laugh, share that moment of happiness
And join in that infectious and insatiable thirst for life.
We could hold that moment so precious to us alone.
We could dream dreams with mike,
We could feel the warmth of that presence larger than life so dear....so dear...
So dear...
We could delight in the joy of fellowship if but for a moment.
We could crop the picture as we would have it.
Then with the shadow of our hand we could accent the lovely
And vignette the not so lovely.

Likely, as Pagliacci though we must smile on the outside
While crying on the inside; such is life.
Lives and hearts are not given to man to use as puppets.

God in His infinite wisdom has reserved divine decisions for himself.
Yes we wish life were bounded by our desires
But then such would just rob us of our Michaels....
And it wouldn't be life... would it?

(10-8-1998 EGH)

The author of this beautiful tribute to our son, John Michael Phillips, is Griffin Harris, Jr., Mike's Scout Master, and our dear Friend!

"SPIRITS"

The world known Symbol of Freedom and Opportunity - The Statue of Liberty. Statue of Liberty used by courtesy of The City of New York.

I came by ship to Ellis Island - to where newcomers are welcomed and processed, and given an opportunity to begin a new life.

I rejoiced in seeing, "The Lady holding high The Torch - bidding Welcome - offering assurance of Freedom and Opportunity!"

I looked back at many of my Heritage - Phillips, Letson, Treadwell, Talley, Goodman, Crittenden, Morgan...... and give Thanks unto God for that, 'Open Door' of Freedom and Opportunity for each of their forebearers, from The Old Country.

But, I also think of those of my Heritage - who were already here, and 'Welcomed' the newcomers and were good neighbors and First Americans!

I want each and every American to help our First American Brothers and Sisters, who were virtually destroyed by the onslaught of the newcomers, and their greed for the land - to enable these Brothers and Sisters of Native American Heritage to return to the great inner strength and self-esteem and self-reliance, as when their forefathers 'Welcomed the newcomers - the pale faced strangers from afar.

May The Great Spirit enable us that it may be - that they be again connected - related to-The Spirit of the Sunlight, The Air, The Wind, The Water, The Mountains, The Land, The Trees - and to all our Brothers and Sisters and to The Great Spirit!!!

So Mote It Be!

SECTION ONE:
NATIVE AMERICAN HERITAGE STORIES

A GREAT LESSON IN HISTORY

I remember with joy and gratitude the privilege of relating to Dr. Herscher, at the excavation of Burnt Indian Village, on the banks of The Chattahoochee River.

About 1966, Forrest Word, Scout Master of The Boy Scout Troop of Shawmut, asked me to go and talk with Dr. Herscher, about The Scout Troop conducting tours of their work at the excavation site of Burnt Indian Village, as a fund raiser for the troop. Dr. Herscher said that he would work with us on one condition, that I come meet with him, walk through his minicourse of archeology, and I would explain to visitors, what the excavation team was doing and why.

I told Dr. Herscher that I didn't have time, as a busy Pastor, to do what he asked of me - but, he would have none of it. After all what could be more important than working with boys of the community, he asked? Today, I am glad that he took the position that he did, for now, I count it a Godsend!! What an opportunity and challenge for the rest of my life, it became!

Two experiences of that mini-course in archeology have greatly impacted and altered my life. The 1st, lesson had to do with Dr. Herscher asking me to scratch around in the village dump, or trash pit for whatever throwaway I might find. When he came back, I told him that I had found virtually nothing but ashes - and he told me that that was the 1st, great lesson that he wanted me to learn - that the Indians did not throw away very much. They made use of most everything that they took from nature or Mother Earth.

The 2nd, lesson was even greater - he showed me the burned remnants of posts, that were part of the round Council House of the village, where he said, "These Indian People practiced the purest form of democracy on earth - Government by CONSENSUS!" Truly, a government of the people, by the people, for the people! According to Lewis Henry Morgan in Ancient Society there were several confederacies in North America. The Iroquois Confederacy of five independent tribes, The Creek Confederacy of Six, The Catawa Confederacy of three, The Dakota League of the "Seven Council-Fires", The Moqui Confederacy in New Mexico of Seven Pueblos, and The Aztec Confederacy of three tribes in the Valley of Mexico. (1) (The Haudenosaunee Nations)

Now, my history education and experiences at Lawrence County High School, Athens College, The University of North Alabama, and Emory University had not prepared me for this encounter, and challenge to my mind and spirit. And these words stuck in my mind, and bugged me until I started to do some serious research to check this out.

My 1st, real encounter in history books, about what Dr. Herscher had said, was in Henry Schoolcraft's works on the History of the Indian Tribes of North America. Dr. Schoolcraft said, "Of the several governments existing in America when it was discovered and settled, none had a system which is at all comparable for its excellence and stability with the Confederacy of the Iroquois. The Iroquois guaranteed to each tribe their tribal or cantonal independence and sovereignty; and at the same time to each man and warrior his equal rights." (2) (Iroquois Confederacy - the Haudenosaunee Nations)

THE MEDALLION I WEAR

My dealings with car salesmen have not been the highest part of my life, but one encounter I will remember for the rest of my life! It was a blessing in the back door.

I listened to a television advertisement of a car, and felt that was an offer that I should respond to. So, I called the salesman, and told him the car we had to trade in. An offer was made, and I said that I would see him in a few minutes. When I walked into the showroom, immediately, he told me that he could not do what he had just offered. I walked out. I needed to walk off some steam.

The author found this Medallion - Symbol of The Rising Sun, when walking along the bank of the Coosa River during the time of repair of The Logan Martin Dam. It was possibly made by a Shaman of The Coosada People about the time Moses received the Ten Commandments, carved in stone.

With an hour on hand, before I was to meet another party, for an appointment, I went to the nearby river, to walk a favorite site, looking for Indian artifacts. I did not know that the river was way down, in order to repair the Logan Martin Dam. I walked about twenty minutes and, "made the find of a lifetime!"

I saw the 'Medallion' about 3 or 4 feet ahead of me, at the edge of the rippling waters, the waves sloshing gently over it, washing it, oh, so beautifully! Surely, I can never forget that 'Moment in Time'! I had goose bumps on goose bumps, as I picked it up! Oh, what a moment, what an experience! I must have stood there a long time, somewhat spellbound - it was a very Spiritual Moment - thinking about who made it, why, when, what it was, what was its significance, what was its message - that Symbol ofThe Rising Sun - that was etched into the stone? It was indeed a very deeply spiritual moment, as I felt that this sacred medallion had been made by a Coosada Spiritual Leader or Shaman, about the time of Moses and The Ten Commandments. I believed, its Message was, 'The Message of Hope!'

Some three days later, I was to speak at a Symposium on the American Indian at Samford University, in Birmingham. I was the sixth speaker. My topic was: 'The Ceremonies of the American Indian'. Before doing my paper, I shared with the group about my find of the 'Medallion', which stirred much excitement and interest. Surely, I can never forget a treasured experience, at the end of the program. Dr. Steve Wimberley, of The University of Alabama Archeology Department, shared a word of affirmation about what I had presented, that means so very much to me to this day! He also, invited me to come meet him, one day soon, and share many notes and concern over a cup of coffee. His sudden and untimely death prevented this from ever happening, to my great sorrow and loss.

After the program was over, I was invited to go with Dr. Linda Martin of The Samford University staff, and meet with the Chief and The Cherokee Council of the Eastern Band of The Cherokee Nation, in Cherokee, North Carolina. In that meeting, there was a picture on the table that was the same symbol as on The Medallion. I requested permission of The Council to use their picture in the books that I was preparing, and they granted it. Though, many of those who were forced to plod 'The Trail of Tears' must have despaired, and felt the final curtain was falling on their noble race, The Great message of the Medallion and the picture was/is "There is a brighter day ahead!" And I believe it is indeed! I have seen much progress toward a better day, in the past 25 years! And May God grant there will be more, much more!

This Symbol. (A Brighter Day Ahead), is the former logo of The Cherokee Children's Home, Cherokee, North Carolina. It is the same Symbol as that on my Medallion, 'The Rising Sun', Symbol of Hope! (Courtesy of The Cherokee Children's Home, Cherokee, N.C.

Entrance into The Oakville Indian Mounds Park, where my Father and all his brothers and sisters were born.

MY FATHERS, WE HAVE SOME UNFINISHED BUSINESS TO DO!

Father (Joseph Robert Phillips, son of William Simmie and Otho Mae Treadwell Phillips, born May 18, 1902, in Oakville, Alabama.), get your walking stick and come on - for you and I have some unfinished business to do. I want to walk over the farm on Trinity Mountain again, just as you and I did right after you and Mother bought it in 1942.

As a boy of 12, I was telling you that I had learned in The 4-H Club about worn out, virtually destroyed and worthless land, where families could not make a living off the land. But, you shared your DREAM of loving this land and rebuilding it, of terracing it to stop those ugly ditches that were eroding and washing the topsoil away, and to plant vetch to plow under as 'green manure', added to that from cleaning the barn and lot. We would 'Learn to Live in Harmony with Mother Earth', and build her up, in the Faith that thereby she will indeed take good care of us. And Daddy, you did work hard at your DREAM, when you were home between jobs of 'helping to build our National War Effort - jobs of powder plants and Oakridge', etc.

The International Friendship Bell and Pavilion honors Manhattan Project workers. It serves as an expression of hope for everlasting peace, friendship and understanding among all people of the world.

Oak Ridge, Tennessee

I remember that time in 1944, when you talked of wanting to go to Cherokee, North Carolina. You wanted Mother to come and go with you. It seemed so very special a trip that you so very much wanted to do. But, I did not understand it at all. Even after visiting there with my young family, and being inwardly drawn back year after year, while the children grew up wanting to go to the beach, rather than back to Cherokee and The Great Smoky Mountains again.

There seemed to be great tension between you and Mother, about that trip to Cherokee - more so even after you made it together - why?

After a Family Reunion, in the Springs Park, Iuka, Mississippi about 1986, I heard someone of the family remark that I had written three histories about our Indian Heritage. They thought that I had heard your Father, my Grandfather Simmie, talk with great pride that we were part Cherokee. That was long years after you and Mother went to visit Cherokee, N.C. That was long years after you and Mother were no longer among us, but had 'gone to The Father's House'. I was stunned, for I had never heard that in my life, (I had written the books as part of my 'Calling to a Missionary concern for The American Indian.) I wish so very much now, that I could explore all of this and understand fully the whole story of any Cherokee Heritage of kinship in our family. For with even that revelation, I began to see many things in my life in a very different way - through different filters.

I remember that often, when you came home on a weekend from The Oakridge Plant that you were helping to build, I asked so many questions about what you were doing. What the plant was, what they would make for the war effort - and I could not understand that you did not know, and that your bosses did not know either? But, now I wish that we had talked about your Cherokee Heritage - when you were a little boy in Oakville - foot racing, wrestling, tracking wild animals, maybe with your neighbor, Jesse Owens - learning to track turkey and deer, and learning to bring home fish and game to help feed the family. What did Grandfather Simmie teach you about your Cherokee People and the Cherokee traditions and ways? Is that how you came to your staunch position and commitment to life - 'my word is my bond'? Is that why you wanted so very much to go to Cherokee, North Carolina? Was that the reason for the tension between you and Mother? Did Mother want to move the family away from the influence of such - "Indian Pride" - , that you moved away from Grandfather, that we left Mississippi, when I was 6 years old, and moved back to Courtland, Alabama? Or, was it that Mother wanted to be among her Letson kinfolk in Lawrence County, Alabama? For the next 10 years - the last years of Grandfather Simmie's life (the only Grandfather I ever knew.), I only saw him on 2 short visits they made to our home, and about 3 or 4 times that we visited them on the farm at the end of the little road. And that was after 1941, when Mother bought a car, and the whole family got together for a 'Special Celebration of The Family Circle'. Grandfather always put great emphasis on "The Family Get-togethers' and on "Keeping the Family Circle Strong!"

Grandfather (William Simmie Phillips, son of John Wiley and Mary Ann Goodman Phillips, born in South Carolina in 1870), get your walking stick and hat, lets go for a walk, for we have some unfinished business to do. As we walk the trail to Brushy Creek, and into Warrior Mountain (which I am sure you knew like the back of your hand), I remember the last day that you and I spent together. I walked with you to get a forked branch of willow. You skinned off the bark, and held the 2 slicky, slimy forks, one in each hand. I followed you, watching in great curiosity - maybe disbelief - as you 'witched for water'. Mother had undoubtedly written that Daddy was much concerned that we did not have adequate water to drink, for cooking, washing clothes, and bathing, etc, though we had 2 wells on the farm or more accurate, we had 2 dry holes on the farm. And you and Grandmother had come from Burnsville, Mississippi-by train? You had come to visit and to witch for water, where we would build the new house.

I watched as you stopped and counted the movements of the tip of the willow fork, up and down-as it responded to the movement of a stream of water, way down in the earth beneath our feet. You told me that it would - I wondered-I doubted-I watched-I heard - but, did I believe, I don't think so, not until the well was drilled and sure enough, 35 feet down there was a good stream of water! Just as you said it would be, Grandfather. Sorry, that I ever doubted.

After the witching was over, we went to sit on the front porch, and look off the mountain, at The Tennessee River in the distance. Grandfather, I asked you where you lived when you were a boy, as I remember it, you told me that you lived in the edge of South Carolina, near the border of North Carolina and Georgia - did I remember it right? Tell me, Grandfather, about your family in Oakville, Alabama. Why did you move to Oakville from White, Georgia? Where did you find Otha Mae Treadwell-my dear-quiet Grandmother? Was that the drawing card that influenced you to move to the area? Did the 1890 strength of the Village of Oakville play a part - or was it the Indian Mounds-Indian Heritage of the area, particularly of The Warrior Mountain? Or, did the fishing and hunting of the area have special appeal, 1st, for your love of the sport, or as its importance as a source of feeding your family. You seemed to be a quiet, confident, resourceful provider from the waters, the ponds, the creeks, the rivers, the forest, and from the good earth! Did you teach the boys - my Daddy, Uncles Albert, Monroe, and Cecil to track game, ways to catch fish in nets, hooks, spears,weirs, grabbling, and crushing green walnuts and using it to stun fish? Did you teach them to be 'Marksmen'-they surely were, both in hunting, and with medals in the army. Did you teach them about the mounds at Oakville, about the traditions of your Cherokee People?

Why did you move away from Oakville — were you an angry old man? — did the sheriff's office putting pressure on families that talked about being Indian or part Indian to leave Alabama — for it was against Alabama Law for such people to live in Alabama — did that have influence on you being called an angry old man, and taking your family and moving into the back-woods - to live way back, at the end of the road in North Mississippi, near the present-day Tombigbee Waterway?

Historical Markers of The Oakville Indian Mound and Cherokee Indian Removal. Nearby my Grandfather, William Simmie Phillips, reared his family and taught them with pride that they were part Cherokee.

Grandfather

Grandfather (Great-grandfather John Wiley Phillips), grab your walking stick, head band or turban, and feathers, hiking bag (for food, water, medicine, etc, needed for such a journey), and come on let's go hike 'The Cherokee Trail' up to Table Rock for, 'we have some unfinished business to do.'

As a small boy, I heard the elders of our family speak of you, as one who had fled or faded into The Great Smoky mountains, as your forefathers before you had done, that you might escape involvement in The Civil War. These elders of the family seemed greatly angered with you for doing that, for they felt you had shunned your proper responsibility as a Southerner.

Today, Grandfather, I hear and see through different filters, that some of these elders of The Family may not have had access to in their day, I imagine, that you being of noble Cherokee Heritage - feeling that you were being forced to take up arms, maybe, even being forced against your will and conviction, to take up arms as a slave, burden bearer of war material and equipment up to the front line, or from one battlefield to another, in a way that you felt was not your Cherokee People's war. Today, as I walk this trail up to Table Rock, we pass by bluff shelters that I imagine was possibly your shelter from the rain, storms, and the snow fall that even now is building up to come tonight.

Will you tell me if The Family Legend is true, or if I have only imagined the tragic lot that became yours to bear - like your kinsmen on 'The Trail of Tears'?

My Granddaughter, Lauren Elizabeth Phillips, assisting me in preparation to tell a Story about The Green Corn Dance.

THE GREEN CORN DANCE

The brown complexioned skin boy, with coarse, straight, black hair, and muscadine looking eyes, runs to his mother, and with great excitement tells her that the corn or maize in the garden is ready for a feast! Hardly able to stand still-to keep from jumping up and down from joy, he tells her that the silks on the ears of corn are brown, dead looking-it is time to gather an arm load and have a great feast, with 'Corn on the Cob!

But, Mother and daddy remind him, that in the American Indian World they never gather and eat of their corn until their People-their village, or tribe have Celebrated The Busk (puskita or busk), or The Green Corn Dance. (1),(2)

The Spiritual Chief or Elder of their People will set a time and call their village or tribe together to celebrate The Green Corn Dance. This most important and Sacred Event is often of eight days in duration. In preparation, there is a time of fasting, a time of spiritual cleansing and renewal of The Ceremonial Square or Plaza, and all public buildings, and all their homes, etc. for this very special Event or Celebration. It is a time for the men to drink the black-drink to purge themselves. The honored old women prepare this black tea from the shrub, Ilex vomitoria. (3), (4), (5), (6)

This Celebration begins with The Myth Keeper or Faithkeeper expressing gratitude to the whole pantheon of spirit forces-the earth, waters, herbs, grasses, saplings, trees, crops, animals, birds, sun, moon, and stars - and to The Creator, The Great Spirit. For some this is part of The Blessings of the Grounds, by The Shaman or Myth Keeper. (7)

The early part of The Celebration is like a great Family Reunion, with much emphasis on visiting, and catching up on all the news of loved ones, friends, and neighbors. It was also the time of the annual clan council, for dealing with problems and concerns for the village or clan, and for the most distinguished member to review the history of the clan for the past year, and give the names of members who deserved to be commended for some deed bringing honor to the clan, or those who had violated tribal laws and dishonored the clan to be shamed. (8)

A 2nd, part of The Green Corn Dance was a focus on children and youth games - like an Olympic Event. There would be foot racing, chunkey, bow and arrow, spear throwing, etc. skill events, stick ball and such. The evenings were spent around campfires, dancing, singing, visiting - enjoying and celebrating being together! The American Indian spent a lot of time and energy teaching and guiding their own children, in their tribal traditions, ways, and beliefs - and I believe it made a very positive difference in their lives. It may well be that that is the reason Thomas Jefferson was quite high on The Indian Culture! (9)

As Hillary Rodham Clinton in *It Takes A Village*, says that she chose the old African proverb to title this book, because it offers a timeless reminder that children will thrive only if their families thrive and if the whole of society care enough to provide for them. The essence of "Village" means the network of values and relationships that support and affect our lives. Our challenge is to arrive at a consensus of values and a common vision of what we can do today, individually and collectively, to build strong families and communities. Creating CONSENSUS in a Democracy depends on seriously considering other points of view, resisting the lure of extremist rhetoric, and balancing individual rights and freedoms with personal responsibility and mutual obligations.

The truest test of the CONSENSUS we build is how well we care for our children. For a child, the village must remain personal. (10)

Another part of The Celebration was the extinguishing of the old fires in their homes and all public buildings, especially The Temple. There was a new fire laid, with logs placed in the Four Cardinal Directions, and The Myth Keeper or Spiritual Chief, The Beloved Man will come forth and prepare or light The Sacred Fire - symbolic of The Presence of The Creator - The Great Sprit with them. Then The Beloved Man will prepare his Pipe, smoke a few puffs-then in an Awesome and Sacred moment, he will offer a puff to The Great Spirit. (11)

The great highlight of this Celebration takes place in a Great Circle. The People gather into a Great Circle, and an old, and honored Spiritual Elder comes forth into the midst of The Great Circle and holding up an ear of corn, reminds all The People that The Corn is a very special Gift of The Great Spirit to their People! The Elder reminds them that it is time to remember and give Thanks and Praise unto the Great Spirit-The Sustainer of Life!

Following a time of Gratitude, Rejoicing, Celebration, and Praise, The People prepare a Great Feast, and enjoy it together! Then, they gather into a Great Circle, or as Charles Hudson in The Southeastern Indians say, "the warriors, their heads covered with white feathers and carrying white feathers in their hands, danced in three concentric circles around the sacred fire." (I wonder at that symbolism-if that symbolism of 3 circles around the Sacred Fire relates to Sun Circles - the most ancient of spiritual symbols etched, pecked, or scratched on many a bluff across this great land.) the Spiritual Leader admonishes the People to resolve all their conflicts and animosities, and live in Harmony. (12)

It was to such a Celebration of the Powhatan Indians, that some very special guest were invited - The Pilgrims! And I imagine that on the way home, they said to one another, "Wasn't that Celebration most impressive and inspiring! In fact, we ought to be ashamed of ourselves-for we sometimes think of them as ignorant savages, and of ourselves as Christians. Yet, we haven't taken time to remember that God has seen us through a terrible winter, and we have a great harvest in the fields - and that we too ought to have a Time of Thanksgiving and Praise unto God! (12a)

They went home, and soon began to plan a time when they would indeed have their own 'Day of Remembrance and Thanksgiving'! As befitting for such special occasion - they invited the Indians as their guests! (13)

Many think of this, Celebration with The Indians, as America's First National Day of Thanksgiving - but, I believe its roots go back hundreds, if not in fact, thousands of years, into The Green Corn Dance - Thanksgiving Celebration of The American Indian! (14)

My grandson, Clint Blackman is pointing to petroglyph of a monolithic ax. There are several etchings on the stone wall in Marion County. Maybe a Chief buried a hatchet here. Since the picture of my grandson is not clear, I have placed another picture of the monolithic ax or hatchet nearby.

BURY THE HATCHET

All my life, I have been intrigued by an old adage- 'Bury The hatchet". I heard the term used many times, as a child, and as a youth, and often, it seemed to have, or be related to a much needed moral lesson, such as: "Resolve that conflict, drop the argument, bury that grudge, or be reconciled."

For many years, as an adult, I have been impressed with The Apostle Paul's admonition, to be reconciled, and especially with Jesus' instruction, "to leave thy gift at the altar, go be reconciled with your brother, then come and offer thy gift. (1), (2)

I turned to The Encyclopedia of Word and Phrase Origins - The Facts on File, by Robert Hendrickson, to check out something of the origin and meaning of the phrase - 'Bury The hatchet'. The author writes that the phrase means, "to settle differences, to let bygones be bygones." It goes back to an old Indian custom. Such ceremony was attached to tomahawks that when peace was made between two tribes, it was customary to take the tomahawks of both chiefs and bury them. When hostilities broke out again, the hatchets were dug up as a declaration of war.

The earliest record of this practice is found in the letters of American author Samuel Sewall, dated 1680. Meeting with the Sachem they came to an agreement and buried 2 axes in the ground-which ceremony to them is more significant and binding than all Articles of Peace, the hatchet being a principle weapon." (3)

Henry Wadsworth Longfellow in his poem about the legend of Hiawatha wrote, "Buried was the bloody hatchet; Buried was the dreadful war-club.... There was peace among the nations." (4)

Recently, in reading in Henry Schoolcraft's work on The American Indian, I found what is probably its origin. In the 'Vision of Deganawidah', The Great Spirit led him to challenge The Iroquois Warriors to bury the hatchets and learn to walk and live together in peace! (5)

Speaking of this custom, Jack Weatherford, in *Native Roots - How The Indians Enriched America*, writes, "Before Deganawidah could make peace among the nations, he needed to banish the Evil Mind that caused fighting and dissension. He persuaded the warriors to bring their weapons to him beside a great tree that grew over an underground cavern. He buried all the weapons deep inside the cavern beneath the tree." Josephy in *The Patriot Chiefs*, reports this in a better way: the mythically fused figure of Deganawidah-Hiawatha said, "We must now work on that which is the guarantee of our welfare.... So that the nations of Natural Man may dwell in peace and tranquillity, undisturbed by the shedding of blood. Into our bundle have we gathered the causes of war, and have cast this bundle away. Yea, we even uprooted a tall pine tree, making a deep hole in the earth, and at the bottom of this hole runs a swift water current. Into this current have we thrown the causes of war and strife. Our great-grand-children shall not see them, for we have set back in its former-place the great tall pine tree." (6), (7)

Thus, under The Great White Pine of Peace, Deganawidah and Hiawatha brought forth an era of Peace and Harmony and Welfare of The Five Nations - The Hau-De-No-Sau-Nee, The League of Nations, The United Nations!

Prayer

O' Great Spirit
Creator of all Life that be,
Who inhabits all the Universe,
And every heart and life,
Guide our feet into The Way of Peace
Into The Ways of Understanding our Brothers,
That under the Great White Pine of Peace,
We may learn, in Consensus,
To live in Peace as Brothers ought!

So may it be.... Amen!.

Calligraphy-Prayer, done by Margurite Busby.

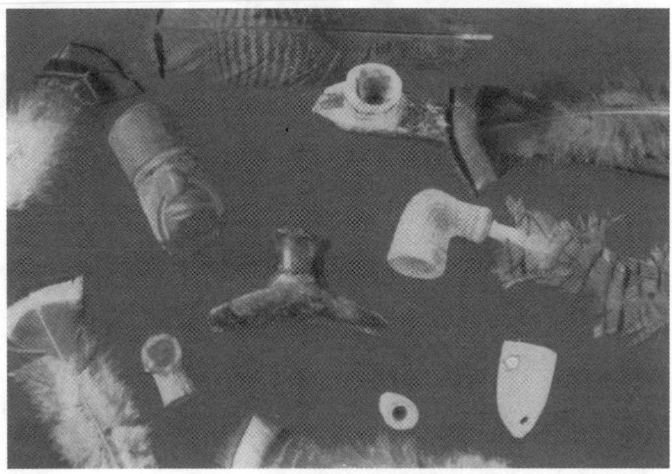

Circle of the Pipes of my Artifact Collection.

THE SACRED PIPE

One afternoon, when I was pastor of The First United Methodist Church of Fayette, Alabama, I went to visit my next door neighbor, who was on the way to becoming 100 years old, (she made it to 104!) She told me that she had heard that her pastor had been going to the schools in the area, telling stories about The American Indian, to the boys and girls.

I told her that I had, sort of expecting next, that she might ask me how I found time for that, with all that I had to do. She did not scold me, in fact, she told me how proud she was that I would take the time to do such, for the boys and girls, and for the school!

She told me that she had three items of Indian Heritage, that belonged to her Mother; that she wanted to give to me. I was overwhelmed - a chisel, a picture of 'The End of The Trail', and most of all, the gift of 'The Hopewell Platform Pipe-a Treasure indeed! I couldn't believe it!

I told her, "Surely, you don't want to give me this family treasure, found by your Mother, so long ago!" (Her Mother found it on the Family farm in Fayette County, not long after The Civil War.)

She assured me that she wanted me to have it, and to use it to tell stories to the boys and girls wherever I could, or had the opportunity to do so. I assured her that I would do so! I also told her that I would like to share one such story with her. Imagine looking down from a high ridge or hill into a valley, where a Great Circle of American Indians were in a Celebration. Into that Great Circle of the People, an old, and honored Spiritual Leader or Elder comes with The Pipe. He holds up The Pipe, reminds The People that The Great Spirit gave them The Pipe to have Communion with Him, and to teach four Great Lessons of Life to the People.

Those Lessons are: 1) Learn to Live in Harmony with The Great Spirit.... (hmm, that is what The Christian Faith is all about). 2) Learn to Live in Harmony with mother Earth, take good care of her and she will take good care of you...(Thanks be unto God, we of America are beginning to learn that Great Lesson of Life!). 3) Learn to Live in Harmony with every weed, and flower, bird and bee, vine and tree - everything that is Alive - for they were made by The Creator that gave you Life and Breath - so they are your Brothers. 4) And Learn to Live in Harmony with our fellowman - live, and walk together in Peace! (1)

Staged scene, with 2 of our Grandchildren, Ashley and Matt Phillips, and an Indian Basket (Cherokee) ladened with good things from my garden. We have done many such scenes in schools, including theirs, telling the Story of the many, many things the American Indian domesticated and shared with the newcomers or colonists, and the world.

TESTIMONIALS OF NOTEWORTHY ACHIEVEMENTS!

As I was preparing to publish the three manuscripts that I had prepared, *The Indian Heritage of Americans, The American Indian In Alabama And The Southeast,* and *Chief Junaluska of The Cherokee Indian Nation,* I wrote to The United States Department of Agriculture to check my work. I told them that according to my research, it seemed that some 40% of the foods that we put on our table today, we owe a debt of gratitude to The American Indian.

They wrote me that I was bad wrong, way off the mark - that it was more like 60 or 65% - more than all of the rest of the human family combined. Now, that was/and is profound! That is truly a great tribute to the great achievements of The American Indian, who through thousands of years of foraging for usable and sustaining food, had discovered, learned about, domesticated, and used a long list of edible produce. Some of it they improved and even hybridized some, which told in its fullness is an amazing Drama of Life Unfolding! But, the best part is how freely they shared these achievements with their neighbors - including The Pilgrims, the folk at Jamestown, at Olde Charles Towne Landing, etc.

Matthew Ross Phillips, our Grandson assisting me in a presentation about American Indian History and Artifacts to his class at The Trussville Middle School.

Our son-in-law, Pete Blackman, and our Grandson, Clint at a place where Native Americans ground corn or acorns for use as food.

A CHOICE WAS MADE - A DIRECTION OF LIFE WAS SET!

Lachlan McGillivray sent his son, Alexander, born of a mother of The Wind Clan, off to get a university education, in hopes that he would become a rich and powerful lawyer.

When Alexander returned home, he chose not to follow the very prosperous ways of Lachlan, but to become a part of his Mother's Creek Indian World, and with his excellent education, he soon was making strides toward gaining places of leadership. In due time, Alexander McGillivray had become 'The Principal Chief of The Creek Confederacy. (1), (2)

In his genius of playing the political forces of France, Spain, England, and The Colonies against each other, in the interest of his Indian People, Chief McGillivray became known as the Talleyrand of America. Much of this achievement was in the meeting and Treaty with President George Washington. (3)

Michael D. Green in a chapter: Alexander McGillivray in American Indian Leaders, edited by R. David Edmunds, writes that in the winter of 1789, President Washington sent a special envoy to McGillivay with an invitation that The Great Beloved Man, along with the headmen of The Creek Nation, come to New York to negotiate,. McGillivray accepted and he and some two dozen Creek leaders spent the summer of 1790 with Washington and Secretary of War, Henry Knox, working out the agreement which, when signed on August 7, 1790, became the Treaty of New York. This treaty was a clear victory for McGillivray. (I have seen this Treaty - on white lambskin - in The National Archives in Washington, D.C., the picture is in my book: *The American Indian in Alabama and The Southeast.* (4)

Chief Alexander McGillivray's Crowning Dream and effort was to establish a 'Union with The Iroquois, Hurons, and Shawnees' - his Dream - strength through union - was a failure. That failure was probably the major cause of his death, through a broken heart! According to legend, he was buried in 'The Masonic Garden' of his dear friend, William Panton, in Pensacola, Florida. The unity of The Creek Confederacy began to dissolve after the death of Chief Alexander McGillivray in 1793. (5)

TOOLS OF THE MEDICINE MAN

Following a graveside service in the cemetery where I am to be buried, I found some evidence of Indian artifact making - chips - flint knapping. There were lots of chips lying around on the ground. That told me one thing for sure, somewhere in time someone had been sitting here on a stump, a log, a boulder, or on the ground flint-knapping, making artifacts. In my imagination, I could see an indian sitting on a stump or great boulder, by a camp fire, and with a hammer stone and deer antler flaking tool, chipping away, making some needed arrow tips, scrapers, spear points, and/or blades, etc.

Tools of a Shaman - an Indian Medicine Man and Spiritual Leader of the people.

After the next big rain, I went back to the cemetery, and I found a treasure - a pecked and ground tool of a Shaman, a Spiritual Chief, or Medicine Man. There are stains on the working end of the small celt, that I imagine being there by the crushing of bark, roots, herbs, etc., in the search for medicinal use and values, needed to care for his people.

Shortly after this find, while doing research in The Public Library of Birmingham, Alabama, I found a book by C. Fayne Porter, *Our Indian Heritage*. He gives the testimonial: "So skillful were the Indian in the knowledge of natural remedies that 'in the four hundred years that the European physicians and botanists have been analyzing and examining the flora of America, they have not yet discovered a medicinal herb not known to the Indian." (1)

In the magazine of The Smithsonian, Native Peoples, 1999 Special Issue - Travel and Destination, in an article titled, "Over 2,000 years of Surgery, Writing prescriptions and Setting Broken Bones. And They Still Haven't Sent Us A Bill." The writer says, "Indian physicians introduced European surgeons to antiseptics and anesthetics. They developed advanced surgical techniques and implements long before their Old World peers. They formulated hundreds of plant-based medicines, including ipecac, quinine, and a headache remedy nearly identical to aspirin. The Indians have greatly valued the Yew's exceptional lung-healing properties for centuries. Its active ingredient, taxol, is one of the most promising cancer drugs in decades. And now it turns out the mayapple, used by Indians to heal skin disorders, contains two new cancer controlling compounds. Potawatomi Indian pharmacists were guided by "formulas" carved into ancient wooden prescriptions sticks that were handed down through countless generations." Soon, in the first museum of its kind - The National Museum of the American Indian - on the Mall in Washington D.C., we will be able to find the opportunity to learn just how much of our life has been shaped and influenced by Native American ideas and values. (I am proud to be a charter member of the NMAI - and you can be too!) To join NMAI call: (800) 242-NMAI. (2)

Goverment by Consensus —
- Democracy -
of the people,
by the people,
for the people.

Great Concepts of the American Indian - Government by Consensus - Democracy - of the People, by the People, for the People! (Calligraphy by Marguerite Busby.)

FREEDOM AND SELF-DETERMINATION

From Time in Memorial, mankind has had a longing - yea, a DREAM OF FREEDOM - of Liberty, and self-determination. The Dream of being Free is as old and universal as mankind. Surely, the Reverend Martin Luther King, Jr., was expressing the yearning of the universal human spirit, in his immortal words, "Free at last, Thank God Almighty, We are Free at last!" (from the classical sermon, "I have a Dream", given on the quadrangle in Washington, D.C.) (1)

About 1400 A.D. a Huron called Deganawidah, had a Vision of a Great White Pine, under which tribes could meet, and with a Great Law of Peace, they could bring Peace, Brotherhood, and Democracy to Mankind. Deganawidah met, and converted to his Vision, an Iroquois, known as Hiawatha, who practiced a ceremonial form of cannibalism. Hiawatha gave up his old ways, and committed himself to this New Vision of Life. (2)

Together, especially through the great persuasive abilities of Hiawatha, they were able through great effort and durability, in time to convince the Sachems or Wise Elders of the Iroquois Nations to give it a try and work with them. And in time, The League of The Hau-De-No-Sau-Nee Nations was established. The 1st, real democracy on earth, where all the people - both men and women - were participants in the decision making affecting their lives! This League of Nations that they established was open to all Tribes, and Nations. And literally in the minds, heart, and intentions of The Hau-De-No-Sau-Nee it was - 'Open to All Peoples", who would trace the 'universal White Roots of the Great White Pine of Peace" to its base or source, and live by The Great Law of Peace. (3) (Edited by Chief Irving Powless, Jr., of The Onondaga Nation of The Hau-De-No-Sau-Nee Nations. He says they did not call themselves Iroquois, or their leaders, Sachems. And that the date it was established should be about 1140 A.D.)

In the 1700's, Hau-De-No-Sau-Nee Wise Elders taught their colonial neighbors about their concepts of Liberty, Freedom, and Self-determination. They also, very much influenced the writings of John Locke, Montesquieu, Rousseau, Thomas Paine, Thomas Jefferson, Charles Thomson, Benjamin Franklin, and others. Most important of all, they invited and or welcomed Colonial Leaders, such as William Penn, Benjamin Franklin, Thomas Paine, Thomas Jefferson, and Charles Thomson to sit in on The Great Council Fires of The Iroquois League or Hau-De-No-Sau-Nee Nations across a span of about a quarter of a century. At a time, when these Colonial Leaders were searching for a usable Model to form a union and government for the colonies, the Hau-De-No-Sau-Nee Wise Elders taught them about a most significant Model of Consensus Government - nothing else like it on earth in that day! (4)

All of this together did much to stir the conflicts, the tensions, anger - to light the coals - the fires of open rebellion - that resulted in The Declaration of Independence from Great Britain, July 4th, 1776! (4)

THE DREAM that birthed THE UNITED STATES OF AMERICA - land of Freedom and Opportunity for ALL - continues to stir the hearts of mankind across the earth! And it has helped to birth THE UNITED NATIONS, and to transform old monarchies into new Democracies - all across the earth!

A GODSEND VISION indeed my Brothers, Deganawidah and Hiawatha!

GREAT IMAGES - SYMBOLS - CONCEPTS OF THE AMERICAN INDIANS

Jim Manesco did a beautiful and intriguing presentation in The Symposium on The American Indian at Samford University, that was sponsored by The Society for The Preservation of The American Indian Culture. Jim talked about Images - petroglyphs - pictographs, etc., that The American Indians have painted, scratched, or etched into stone, on or around boulders, and on the side of bluffs all across this continent. They are innumerable, and they are National Treasures! Mr. Manesco also suggested that they have a Message. And, he interpreted some of them. His idea and presentation impressed me.

The author believes that President Woodrow Wilson built his concept of The League of Nations on the great vision of Deganawidah.

I did not think about it at the time, but after Jim spoke, I came forth to do my paper on The

Ceremonies of The American Indian. I began by sharing a word about a Medallion that I had found, only 2 or 3 days before, on The Coosa River, and was wearing it that day. The Medallion had a Symbol of The Rising Sun etched into it. I declared that I believed that symbol was a 'Message of Hope'. Later, I found such a symbol in an old encyclopedia on art, in the Public Library in Fayette, Alabama. It called the symbol - the rising sun. But, what meant more to me was and is the remembrance that Dr. Steve Wimberley, Archeologist of The University of Alabama, almost ran to the podium, looked at The Medallion, and said it was indeed a Symbol of The Rising Sun, a Symbol of Hope, and a treasure find of a lifetime!

The more I thought about it, the more I was caught up with the idea that The American Indian did in fact evolve - bring forth and give to the human family many Great Concepts. Among them, their concept of personal or individual liberty, of self-government, of government by consensus, and leadership based on the respect and esteem of the people. Cadwallader Colden, in 1727, wrote that, 'Each Nation is an absolute Republic by its self, govern'd in all Public Affairs of War and Peace by the sachems or Old Men, whose Authority and Power is gain'd by and consist wholly in the opinion the rest of the nation have of their Wisdom and Integrity. They never execute their Resolutions by Compulsion or Force upon any of their people. Honor and Esteem are their Principal Rewards, as Shame and being Despised are their Punishments." Surely, the greatest concept relating to government is: of the people, by the people, for the people! These concepts have etched themselves on the minds, and into the spirits of the people of The Thirteen Colonies, becoming The United States of America, helping to birth nations of democracy across the earth, The League of Nations, and The United Nations! (1), (2), (3)

SEQUOYAH - AND THE TALKING LEAVES!

Sequoyah, though never an elected chief of The Cherokee Indian Nation, or even chief of a Cherokee village, was none the less, a great and honored leader of his beloved Cherokee People. In fact, because of his amazing achievements and contributions, he was a profound leader of his people. Truly a genius of the whole human family. By many, he is called - and fittingly so, it seems to me - Chief Sequoyah.

Sequoyah was born in Tennessee about 1770, according to James H. O'Donnell, III, in Southern Indians in The American Revolution. He writes that, "Colonel Nathaniel Gist was commissioned by General George Washington, to recruit among the Cherokee, to enlist four companies of rangers and several hundred Cherokees to serve as scouts. His years as a trader, his marriage alliance within the tribe, and his overall standing with the Cherokee guaranteed him their attention." (In a footnote on page 56 - "Nathaniel Gist, Father of Sequoyah.") (1), (1a), (2)

My Friend, Rickey "Butch" Walker, in Warrior Mountains Folklore says, "Sequoyah's Mother, Wut-the, was the sister of Tahlenteeskee (the Overthrower) and Doublehead, who controlled the Lawrence County area for their Cherokee People or Cherokee Nation." (3)

My Friend, William Lindsey McDonald, in Lore of The River-The Shoals of Long Ago says, "Doublehead, or 'Talo Tiske', meaning two heads, and sometimes 'Autowe', was a member of a prominent Cherokee family. One of his brothers was the beloved statesman, "Tassel", or "Old Tassel", a principle chief of the Cherokee Nation, who became the parents of the most

Statue of Sequoyah in The Oakville Indian Museum, used in this book, courtesy of Butch Walker, and The Oakville Indian Museum.

famous Cherokee of all, the notable Sequoyah. Another of Doublehead's sisters married a Fort Loudoun soldier. Their offspring became the bold and magnanimous John Watts, who at one time was counted as the chief of chiefs among all the Cherokees. (4)

As many Indians, the young Sequoyah had a problem with alcoholic beverages. At this point of need of help with low self-esteem, George Lowery, a Cherokee friend, played a most significant part or influence in the greatness or achievements of Sequoyah. George Lowery certainly proved the Friend, when he helped reclaim Sequoyah from alcoholism, one of the ills and hindrances of The American Indian. (5)

In October, 1813, Sequoyah or George Gist volunteered to assist General Andrew Jackson and The Tennessee Militia in The Battle of Horseshoe Bend against the rebel Creeks, who were called, 'The Red Sticks'. (6)

I imagine Sequoyah sitting around the camp fire at night watching White soldiers read letters from home, write letters home to family, or maybe even someone reading a tattered old Bible. And, he became very much impressed with the power the Whites seemed to find in and through 'The Talking Leaves'. And he longed to be able to give this power to his Cherokee People. (7)

When, he returned home, from the war with the Red Sticks, he began to dream of achieving this great feat. He tried to make symbols for Cherokee words. James Mooney in Historical Sketch of The Cherokee writes that the years of frustrating effort of Sequoyah to use the idea of Indian pictographs for Cherokee words. Then in finding a white man's book, he learned a great fact, that writing was based on using symbols for various sounds. He now formulated a symbol for each Cherokee sound. In time he had 85 symbols for the Cherokee syllabary. And then a Cherokee youth or adult could learn to read and write in the Cherokee language in a few days! And they did - almost the entire Cherokee Nation! (8) Others say that it was after his wife threw all his work into the fire and destroyed it. He took Ah-Yoka, his little daughter, and left home. Then one day, Ah-Yoka found a book, and brought it to him. Sequoyah studied it carefully, and determined the strange marks - letters of the English alphabet - were for 26 different and various sounds, and were used over and over again, in writing words. Now - he realized their secret - thus, he began to work with renewed confidence of finding symbols that would represent the various sounds of the Cherokee language. And in time, he had developed an 85 syllabary - and he and Ah-Yoka could communicate with them!

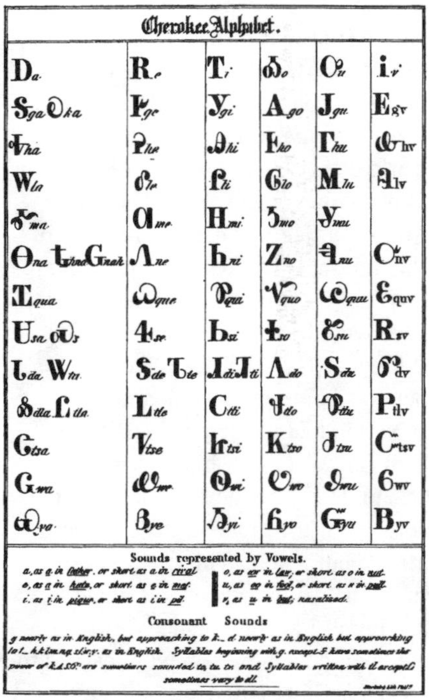

The Cherokee Syllabary invented or developed by Sequoyah.

from History of The Indian Tribes of The United States, 1852, by Henry R. Schoolcraft

Now, he needed an opportunity to prove it - but, he had a severe and serious problem, for at the same time, there were fellow Cherokee who thought he was crazy, and wanted the Council to try him as a witch. But, his friend of many years, George Lowery, was able to get him a hearing to demonstrate for The Council how he and Ah-Yoka could pass messages with the new syllabary and his 'talking leaves', instead of carrying him through a witch trial and execution. (11a), (11)

In *Indian Chiefs*, Lynne Deur writes that, "He and his daughter, Ah-Yoka returned east and met with a Cherokee Council. The believing council members gave Ah-Yoka several sentences to

Marker of Sequoia National Park - Tribute to the great achievements of Sequoyah.

Base of a Huge Sequoia Tree

write down. Then Sequoyah, who had been out of the room, returned and read aloud the sentences from Ah-Yoka's paper. the Indian leaders were stunned, and then, overjoyed. At last The Cherokee could have a written language! (12)

Of this most significant achievement, James Mooney in *Historical Sketch of The Cherokee* writes about 3,000 years of work that was involved in bringing forth the current English language. But, Sequoyah, though uneducated and with little help, brought forth the Cherokee syllabary in a few years, that enabled the Cherokee Nation to become a literate people almost overnight! (13)

Truly, Sequoyah's work in creating the Cherokee Syllabary and teaching his Cherokee People to read and write their own language was and is a world class achievement! Unique among all the achievements of the human family! And soon Sequoyah could rejoice for many of his fellow Cherokee were learning to read and write their Cherokee language, parts of The Bible were being translated into The Cherokee tongue, The Cherokee Phoenix Newspaper was being published, and The Cherokee Nation had written a Constitution and Code of Laws! (14) a, b, c.

Illustration of Sequoyah by Jason Michael Phillips.

My Friend, Homer Noley, in First White Frost, wrote about the great success of the literary movement among The Cherokees. It was due to their 'using the method (that Missionary Frank Laubach made world famous) of having each person who learned the alphabet teach another Cherokee, the system swept through the community until there was scarcely anyone who could not read or write their Cherokee language. (15)

Grant Foreman in *The Five Civilized Tribes* writes that, "The Cherokee people were appreciative of the great service of Sequoyah. They sought to show their gratitude in a manner explained by Chief Ross: "Head of Coosa, Cherokee, January 12, 1832, Mr. George Gist; My Friend: The legislative Council of the Cherokee Nation in the year 1824 voted a medal to be presented to you, as a token of respect and admiration for your ingenuity in the invention of the Cherokee alphabetical characters." (16)

Through it all, Sequoyah had become an honored and beloved member of The Cherokee Nation! (16a),

Illustration by Jason Michael Phillips about the birth of democracy in a Great Council Fire gathering of 50 Wise Elders of The Hau-De-No-Sau-Nee People, led and challenged by Hiawatha and Deganawidah.

THE GREAT COUNCIL FIRE!

One of the most exciting moments, in all of my research, was that of reading for the first time, the story of the fiery challenge of Chief Tecumseh, to The Choctaw warriors.

Chief Pushmataha sent runners out - all across The Choctaw Country - to call the warriors of his people, to gather for a 'Great Council Fire' - somewhere near Fort St. Stephens. A Great Circle of warriors gathered about 'The Great Council Fire', (it must have been a most moving and impressive sight to behold - a great roaring fire, a Great Circle of painted, and feathered, and armed Warriors, in hours of heated debate!) And, they listened with quiet, but deadly seriousness, to the long and fiery speech of Tecumseh - 'calling upon his Indian Brothers to unite, and drive the White man out of their ancestral homeland, and from these shores!' The Great Circle of Warriors also listened to their Chief, Pushmataha, rebuff Tecumseh, and pledge his support for 'Peace with their White friends and neighbors of The Tombigbee Country! (1)

They also heard their Chief, Pushmataha, say the decision would not be made by the two leaders or Chiefs, but, that each warrior might step forth, speak their views and convictions on the issue before them, and then cast their vote for war or for Peace. (2)

When the speaking and voting was finished, the vast majority had cast their vote (war club) for Peace with their White neighbor! (A side was designated for Peace votes, and a side or area around The Great Council Fire was designated for war votes, they pitched their war club accordingly.) To me, this was and is a great story of Democracy Alive and in Action! (3), (3a)

May it ever be so! And may Democracy - government of the People, by the People, for the People - spread forth throughout the whole wide earth, until all of God's Children are Free.

This generation has seen more Democracies born across the earth, than all other generations of all time combined! May it soon reach the ends of the earth - that all Mankind may live in Peace and in Harmony!!

A Circular palisaded village - from the historical marker at The Welcome Center on I 59 south of Fort Payne.

THE GREAT CIRCLES OF LIFE

There are many very significant, very spiritual symbols in The American Indian World. One of these is The Great Circle, which is so very much a part of Native American Spirituality.

The other Sunday, as I sat down to worship, in The First United Methodist Church of Troy, Alabama, the many beautiful circles of the sanctuary reminded me of this symbolism of Native American Spirituality.

The Circle of Life is symbolic of each individual life, which is a Great Gift of The Creator or Giver of Breath. It is symbolic of The Family Circle, where each child is guided and protected and sustained, as Chris Roberts in an article: "Children of The Circle", in the magazine, Native Peoples, describes about Pow-Wows and Tribal Ceremonies and Dances. (1)

There has been much excitement this week about an Ancient Great Circle found in The City of Miami, Florida. It surely is a Sacred Site of native American Spirituality significance, and hopefully through a Federal Law: Eminent Domain, it will be preserved and protected as part of a National Historical Site! (2)

The Circle of Life also represents the larger family, kinfolk, or clan; the village; the tribe; the Hoop of The Nation, and Nations. And in The Vision of Deganawidah, it represents The Circle of The United Nations of all the earth, that meets at its headquarters in New York, USA! But, above all else, it represents The Creator and Sustainer of Life!

This significant symbol of The American Indian World was often seen and expressed in The Ceremonies and Celebrations of The American Indian. It was very much a part of The Green Corn Dance, of The Sacred Pipe Ceremonies, of The Great Council Fires, and many other such Sacred Events of The American Indian World. Surely, a most meaningful and impressive moment would have been to be part of a Great Circle solemnly passing The Pipe-Remembering that we are Brothers by The Creation, Will, and Design of THE CREATOR, THE GREAT SPIRIT!

'HIAWATHA - A FOUNDING FATHER OF DEMOCRACY'

Hiawatha seems to burst forth upon the stage of human events out of the shadowy and gorgeous precincts of mythology, where the imagination has free scope in accounting for the origin and rise of nations, institutions, and customs; so writes Henry Schoolcraft about 1850. (1)

Hiawatha met the visionary Huron elder named Deganawidah, who was preaching a message of The Great Law of Peace, thirteen laws by which people and nations could live in peace and unity - a democracy where the needs of all would be accommodated without violence or bloodshed. At the time, Hiawatha was melancholy, in exile after the death of his last daughter, and was a cannibal (some Iroquois followed the practice of eating parts of enemies who possessed desired strength in arms, fleet of foot, brave heart, keen mind, etc. to gain that coveted strength for themselves.). He was persuaded to give up his evil and despondency, and join Deganawidah's crusade. (2), (3)

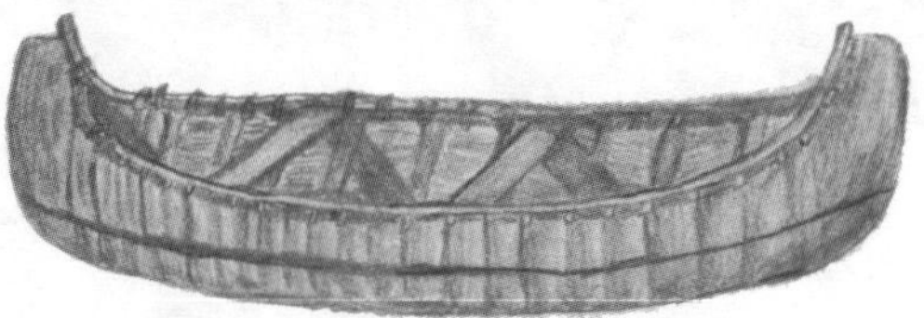

Illustration of Hiawatha's beautiful, white, birchbark canoe by Jason Michael Phillips.

Hiawatha, in his beautiful and magnificent canoe, which as Henry Schoolcraft writes, "Was of the purest whiteness (white birch bark), and appeared to move, when he was seated in it, with the power of magic. With the touch of his paddle it ascended the rapids of the Oswego river. In this canoe, he ascended all the lesser lakes, carefully examined their shores, and placed all things in proper order for the sustenance and comfort of good men. He had taught the people of the different tribes the art of raising corn and beans - articles which had not before been cultivated among them. He made the fishing grounds free, and opened to all the uninterrupted pursuit of game. He had distributed literally among mankind the good fruits of the earth, and had removed all obstructions to the navigation of the streams. He now directed and encouraged the people every where to a more faithful observance of the laws and requirements of the great and good Spirit, that these blessings might be perpetually continued to them, and that the nations he had visited might be the favored recipients of his choicest bounties." (4)

Illustration of Hiawatha with his Sacred Pipe (passport), and his Hiawatha Wampum Belt, in his beautiful, white, birchbark canoe by Jason Michael Phillips, Indian by Benny Yates, Wampum Belt by Hiawatha.

Hiawatha made a wampum belt recording The Great Law of Peace of Deganawidah. And now, in his beautiful, white, birch-bark canoe, and with his Hiawatha Wampum belt, he went among all The Iroquois Tribes or Nations preaching and teaching The Great Law of Peace. He was persuading them to accept (5) Deganawidah's new democracy league concept, and to work together and live in Peace and Harmony as Brothers ought. He even converted the evil wizard, Atotarho, and persuaded him to be a champion of The Great Law of Peace, and to bring his Onondaga Tribe into The League. (6), (7)

Hiawatha met with The Grand Council of 50 Sachems (Wise Men) and laid before them Deganawidah's plan of union - The Great Law of Peace - and said to them, "By uniting in a common bond of brotherhood, we may hope to succeed-Brothers - if we unite in this bond The Great Spirit will smile upon us, and we shall be free, prosperous, and happy."

There are many great Symbols in this picture - The Great White Pine of Peace, The Hiawatha Wapum Belt on Hiawatha's arm, the Sacred Pipe (passport among the Nations), The Beautiful, White Birchbark Canoe of Hiawatha, the Watchful Eye of the Eagle, and Hiawatha seeking to convince his Hau-De-No-Sau-Nee People to form the League or Union of Nations - The 1st, Democracy!!

Illustration of Hiawatha by Jason Michael Phillips.

Illustration of Hiawatha -- canoe by Jason Michael Phillips, Indian by Benny Yates, Wampum Belt by Hiawatha, beautiful scene courtesy of Michigan Travel.

The Chiefs, after due deliberation, again assembled, and declared the counsel of the wise man (Hiawatha) to be good, and worthy of adoption; and immediately was formed the celebrated League of The Great Confederacy of Five Nations - The League of The Hau-de-no-sau-nee. (8)

Hiawatha now spoke to the people, "I have now assisted you to form an everlasting league and covenant of friendship - Listen, my friends; the great Master of Breath calls me to go; I have patiently waited his summons; I am ready - farewell." (9)

Hiawatha was soon seen majestically seated in his necromantic (means of communicating with the realm of the dead where all his family were), canoe. He rose gracefully from the council-grounds, rising higher and higher through the air, until he became nearly lost from view of the assembled and admiring throngs, while the fascinating music gradually became more and more plaintive and low, and finally it sweetly expired in the softest tones upon their ears as Hi-a-wat-ha, the godlike Ta-ren-ya-wa-go entered the celestial regions of Owayneo.

Such is the legend which the fancy of the Onondaga has constructed to account for the origin of the ancient league once formed by the warlike and illustrious Five Nations. In *Manabozho - The Indian's Story of Hiawatha*, Alden O. Fleming had Hiawatha to say, "Farewell, my good friends, I am on my way to join those in the land of the great Gitche Manito. I shall see my beloved Minnehaha again." (10), (11), (12)

'NATIVE AMERICAN INDIAN SPIRITUALITY'

Tonight, I wear a Symbol that evolved out of Native American Spirituality. It is primitive folk art - Symbol of The Rising Sun-Symbol of Hope! I found the medallion, on the bank of the Coosa River, near 1-20 Interstate Highway, a few days before I was to speak in a Symposium on The American Indian at Samford University, in Birmingham, Alabama. Before presenting my paper, on Ceremonies or Rituals of The American Indian, I shared about the medallion. I told them that I imagined it was made and worn by a Shaman of The Coosada People of The Coosa River Basin, in the Woodland Period, about the time that God through Moses gave us The Ten Commandments. It speaks of a Spirit of Faith and tenacity in Native American People that will not die!

As we talk about Native Spirituality, we need to do so with the understanding that there are many differences among Indians. They are not all the same, even as other peoples are not the same.

Yet, there are some historians, who hold that there are some fairly universal things that we can say about The Indian's Spirituality. They believed in a Supreme Being — The Master or Giver of Breath — The Creator — The Great Spirit, and The Happy Hunting Ground!

Like most primitive people, The Native American People were superstitious. They had many beliefs about various spirits or gods, that caused the bad things that happened to them. (1)

Many of those who sought to interpret Indian history did so without much, or, in some cases, any effort whatever, to understand and appreciate them, their beliefs, values, and achievements. Too often, too much, many of these evaluations were made through their European beliefs, values, and experience filters. These writers saw, and heard the Indian's expressions about fire, the sun, moon, eagles, etc. as paganism or as polytheism. (2)

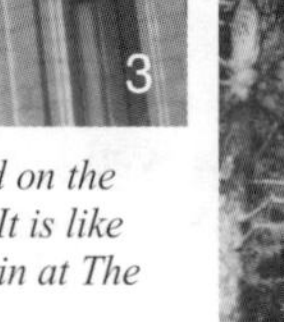

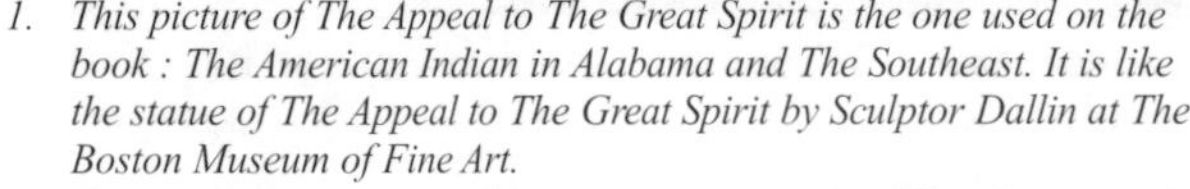

1. *This picture of The Appeal to The Great Spirit is the one used on the book : The American Indian in Alabama and The Southeast. It is like the statue of The Appeal to The Great Spirit by Sculptor Dallin at The Boston Museum of Fine Art.*
2. *Picture of Appeal to The Great Spirit given me by a friend, Reverend Bill Hart.*
3. *Sculpture of The Appeal to The Great Spirit by Sculptor Dallin at The Boston Museum of Fine Art. Photograph by Susan McCoy, the author's niece.*
4. *Statue of Appeal to The Great Spirit in Indiana, picture given me by Brother-in-law, Carl Ridge.*

It would be interesting to take this same basis of evaluation, and interpret what we see in the stained glass windows and alcoves of many a beautiful sanctuary today.

On the other hand, some like James Adair, who went and lived among tribes of the Southeast - The Creeks, or Muskhogean Peoples, The Cherokees, The Chickasaws, and The Choctaws - for some 40 years, and gained much understanding and appreciation of these peoples, and their beliefs, expressions, and achievements; often, by asking their elders, what they meant; then wrote with a very different evaluation. Adair learned from these elders that their reverence for fire was that they felt it was a gift from The Great Spirit. It was so very important in their lives, for warmth, cooking, light, and protection from dangerous, wild animals. And fire was held in Indian belief to be a Representative of The Great Spirit among them. We may even note here something akin to our United Methodist Symbol of The Cross and Flame - which does not mean that we worship fire, but rather that we feel the flame represents The Presence and Power of The Holy Spirit in our lives and in our world - God Present with us! (3)

Some, thus began to hear the Indian's use of, or emphasis on the eagle, to be somewhat like the writer of Holy Scriptures, who said, "They that wait upon The Lord, shall renew their strength, they shall mount up with wings like eagles, they shall run and not be weary, they shall walk and not faint." The Prophet Isaiah was not worshipping the eagle, but rather using the people's regard and appreciation of the eagle's great strength to fly and to soar to great heights, even in the midst of great turbulence and storms, as a symbol, to express his faith, that they who open their minds and lives to The Lord - and wait upon The Lord - shall gain great strengths to face the storms of life, and to endure! (4)

I believe, that we can best understand Native Spirituality by looking at some of their Ceremonies-such as: 1) Blessing of The Grounds, 2) The Green Corn Dance, and 3) the use of symbols of The Circle of Life, The Passing of The Peace Pipe, and The Hiawatha Wampum Belt of Unity, Harmony, Brotherhood, and Peace. (5)

The Indians felt that corn or maize was a very special Gift of The Great Spirit. When the corn was ready to eat as, 'corn on the cob', The Chief, most likely the Shaman or Spiritual Chief of the village or tribe, would set a time to Celebrate the annual Green Corn Dance. The indications are that everyone came, for the 4 to 8 days of Celebration. It was a time of fellowship or 'Reunion', of singing and dancing, of feasting, and of Renewal, and Thanksgiving. The high moment-very Sacred Moment-was when an honored elder or grandfather of the village or tribe would come forth into the midst of The Great Circle of The People and prepare his Pipe. He would smoke a few puffs, and then in evident great awe or reverence, hold The Pipe bowl in both hands, and hold the stem very high for The Great Spirit to likewise take a few puffs. For The American Indian, this was a very high and holy or Sacred moment of Holy Communion with The Giver and Sustainer of Life! Now, there was much emphasis of Thanksgiving unto The Great Spirit for the Gift of Corn. Then, there was an emphasis on The Great Principles that The Great Spirit had taught them or given them through the use of The Pipe. (6), (7)

An honored Elder or Spiritual Leader would remind them of the 4 great lessons - 1) Learn to Live in Harmony with The Great Spirit, 2) Learn to Live in Harmony with mother Earth, for she is our Mother, 3) Learn to Live in Harmony with all living things for they are our Brothers, and 4) Learn to Live in harmony with our fellowman. My Father's number one rule of life was: 'My word is my Bond.' (8)

Following this very awesome and very reverent moment in The Green Corn Dance, when no one dared move or create the least commotion or distraction, not even the little children, the people were directed to go gather the new Corn - the roasting ears-corn on the cob-and prepare a Great Feast, for a time of Great Celebration and Thanksgiving! (9)

At the end of The Green Corn Dance, The Shaman or Chief Spiritual Leader of the group or village would come forth and talk with The Great Circle of The People about their Community-their relationship with each other. Those who had differences or animosities were admonished to resolve them, to be reconciled-to Bury The hatchet - that they might end The Green Corn Dance in Great harmony! One Goal was to walk together in Peace and Harmony - caring for one another! (10)

Rock Art by the American Indian. This composite of art done by Benny Yates is based on a group of photographs the author made across the area.

DEGANAWIDAH AND THE GREAT VISION

In the dim and distant past, there was a custom between The American Indian of 'Seeking Your Vision'.

Deganawidah, of The Huron Tribe, would have been influenced by this strong custom or tradition of his people. I imagine him having been given a Pipe by the elders of his family, clan or village, and being admonished to seek his vision.

I imagine, Deganawidah, rising very early one morning, long before the break of day, to go to a favorite site for him. It was the shade of a great white pine on a knoll, overlooking a beautiful lake. There was a cavern into the bowels of the earth, beneath the pine. This was a place he loved to go to, he loved to explore the cavern - imagining, he was slaying dragons, and often going skinny dipping in the cool, and oh, so clear and clean waters of the lake. And, then his favorite thing to do was to take a nap, in the wonderful shade of the great white pine-oh, how he loved this place - and especially The Great White Pine!

On this special morning, he sat on the knoll smoking The Sacred Pipe of his People. He was mediating about life-and his people and warring - bloodshed - things were not as they ought to be among the people. He was communing with The Great Spirit - he began to feel caught up in The Spirit-and as the Sun began to rise, he has a Vision of Life! It was a Vision of The Great Spirit, saying to him that he was unhappy with the warring and bloodshed among his people, which was not the way He willed the people to live. The Great Spirit told him that he was to go challenge all the warriors of his people to bring their hatchets and war clubs, and bury them in the great cavern. Then, sitting together under The Great White Pine and talking with each other, and listening to each other, and learning to walk together as Brothers, in Peace and Harmony! (1)

He resolved to go convince The Iroquois warriors of the merit of his great Vision, but, he had a problem, he could not speak very well, he stuttered very badly. But, The Great Spirit led him to a (2) coworker - Hiawatha, who was a very capable speaker. And the two became as one. United, and working together, in a great Unity of Spirit and Harmony of Purpose, they were able to bring the Five Nations - Mohawk, Oneida, Cayuga, Onondaga, and Seneca into a Union of Nations - The League of The Iroquois - The Hau-De-No-Sau-Nee! (3)

The Great White Pine - limbs are generally in Great Circle - about the trunk of the tree, and the limbs are usually of somewhat equal size and space - seeming basis, for them, for the Concept of The Council of Wise Elders of The Hau-De-No-Sau-Nee Nations. (edited by Chief Irving Powless, Jr., of The Onondaga Nation of The Hau-De-No-Sau-Nee Nations.)

THE GREAT WHITE PINE OF PEACE'

One of the most significant symbols of The Native American World is that of The Hiawatha Wampum Belt. It is a tribute of Great Achievement!

The 1st, thing that stands out in this Symbol is The Iroquois Brothers joining hands, living, talking, walking, and working together in Harmony and Peace as Brothers ought. The Hiawatha Wampum Belt is a Symbol of The Five nations of Iroquois People learning to live together peacefully and in Harmony. It is the beginning of the oldest, continuous story of the democracies on earth. Jack Weatherford in Native Roots, write that, "The Hiawatha Belt signifies the union of the nations of the Hau-De-No-Sau-Nee, the Iroquois League, founded approximately six hundred years ago by Deganawidah and Hiawatha." (1), (2) *(edited by Chief Irving Powless, Jr., of the Onodaga Nation of the Hau-De-No-Sau-Nee. He says it was founded about 1140 AD.)*

The 2nd, thing that stands out in this Great Symbol is the tree - Deganawidah's Symbol of The Great White Pine of Peace. The Great Tree of Peace spoke a Message of Inspiration, of Challenge, of Hope! Its Message was that ALL NATIONS, who would come sit together as Brothers, accepting each other, listening to each other's views, feeling, and concerns; and acknowledging each other's concerns, needs, and wishes; they would learn to 'Live Together in Harmony and Walk Together in Peace!' At the birth of The League of The Hau-De-No-Sau-Nee or Iroquois League of Nations, Deganawidah planted a Great White Pine that became a great symbol of Peace. Deganawidah and Hiawatha declared this Great Message to The Iroquois People and about 1400 A. D. the Mohawk, the Seneca, the Onondaga, the Oneida, and the Cayuga formed a union or confederacy. (3) *(edited by Chief Irving Powless, Jr., of the Onondaga Nation, he says the date is about 1140 AD.)*

Hiawatha and Deganawidah proclaimed in their Message that people of other nations would be Welcome into 'The Shade of The Great White Pine of Peace', with The Council of The Iroquois Confederacy.(4) And they came - French, British, Scotchmen, Dutch, and Colonial Leaders, such as Benjamin Franklin, Thomas Jefferson, William Penn, etc. And in time, influenced by the 'Vision of Deganawidah', and the wisdom and advice and counsel of The Sachems or Wise men of The Iroquois, I believe, they fulfilled the 2nd, Vision of Deganawidah, that such would bring forth a New Nation. This I believe, was the birth of The United States of America! Jack Weatherford in Native Roots writes that, "Deganawidah prophesied that the roots of the tree would eventually grow to the far parts of the world, that in time the four roots would eventually grow to the far parts of the world, that in time the four roots would grow to include new nations of people not yet known. From many nations they would create one." (5)

And indeed, we have come together at Independence Hall, Philadelphia - of many peoples - from all over the earth - we have come together and formed a New Nation — ONE NATION, UNDER GOD, WITH LIBERTY AND JUSTICE FOR ALL! — THE UNITED STATES OF AMERICA!

What a Symbol of a Great Council of Five Iroquois Nations-a Great Circle of Brothers Passing The Sacred Pipe of Peace, Sealing The Bonds of Unity, Brotherhood, Harmony, and Peace!

The Great Council Fire of The Hau-De-No-Sau-Nee, The Great Circle of The Wise Elders of The Iroquois, illustration done by Jason Michael Phillips.

HAU-DE-NO-SAU-NEE, LEAGUE OR UNITED NATIONS OF THE IROQUOIS

The legend of the beginnings of The League, according to Henry Schoolcraft's *History of The Indian Tribes of The United States*, is that "perhaps 1000 years before Columbus discovered the America", The Five Nations became independent nations. This view is that they were established nations about 492 A. D. Alvin M. Josephy, Jr., in 500 Nations, writes that they were well established Iroquois Nations by 1000 A. D. (This is what I felt Schoolcraft intended.) In Indian Giver, Jack Weatherford writes, "Hiawatha and Deganawidah founded the League of the Iroquois sometime between A. D. 1000 and 1450, under a constitution they called the Kaianerekowa or Great law of Peace." (1), (2), (3) *(edited by Chief Irving Powless, Jr., of the Onondaga Nation. He says the date was about 1140AD.)*

As we first see these Iroquois Nations, they are living in a strong tradition of blood revenge (an eye for an eye, and a tooth for a tooth, as in The Old Testament.), with great suffering and loss of life, if not in fact, even threatening to destroy each other. Then, about 1400 A.D. a new era began to dawn. (4)

In America's Fascinating Indian Heritage, the author reports that, "According to Indian Mythology, the first Iroquois to express horror at the fraternal warfare among the Iroquois Tribes was a holy man named Deganawidah. Said to be born of a virgin mother in the mid-16th, century (some accounts have him arising a hundred years earlier.), he is alleged to have had a vision about 1570 in which he saw the union of the Five nations. The Iroquois, he said, must cease warring upon one another and unite under the sheltering branches of a symbolic Tree of Great Peace." (5)

According to Arnold Marquis, in a Guide to America's Indians, "An Iroquois Chief, the real Hiawatha, preached that the tribes were destroying each other and urged them to join in an alliance for the common good. Hiawatha's proposal stirred so much opposition that he had to flee for his life. In the wilderness he found an ally, another refugee, a Huron named Dekanawida, together they visited the warring tribes and promoted the alliance. The result was the Iroquois Confederacy." (6)

In Our Indian Heritage, C. Fayne Porter says, "The old Iroquois creation myths say that Teheronhiawagon, the Master of Life, had created man to live at peace with his brothers. The Master of Life had further promised that, when the need was great enough, he would send a man among them to insure that the peace of Teheronhiawagon would be carried out. "With the appearance of Hiawatha and Deganawidah it seemed the fulfillment of The Promise of Teheronhiawagon." (7)

Hiawatha and Deganawidah called the wise men or sachems of the Five Iroquois Nations together in Council and laid before them Deganawidah's Plan of Union - The Great Law of Peace-and in due time, they debated until they reached agreement - CONSENSUS - and formed The League of The Hau-De-No-Sau-Nee-The League of The Longhouse. (8)

Some longhouses of The Iroquois were as much as 300 feet long and housed many families of a clan together. The Iroquois conceived of The Hau-de-no-sau-nee as a Family of The Longhouse some 300 miles long, united, and living together in Peace and Harmony!

In Ancient Society, Lewis Henry Morgan writes that, "When the confederacy was formed, about A. D. 1400-1450, the conditions previously named were present. The Iroquois was in five independent tribes, occupied territories contiguous to each other, and spoke dialects of the same language which were mutually intelligible. Common gentes (sense of kinship, of being family) afforded a natural and enduring basis for a confederacy.... The formation of a confederacy became a question of intelligence and skill... The fact that the Iroquois tribes accomplished the work affords evidence of their superior capacity. 3) The Iroquois claimed that it had existed from one hundred and fifty to two hundred years when they first saw Europeans. The generations of sachems in the history by David Cusick (a Tuscarora), would make it more ancient. In the League of the Hau-De-No-Sau-Nee or Iroquois, Lewis Henry Morgan, with Seneca Sachem, Do-ne-Hau-ga-wa, wrote, "We constitute but one house, we five Iroquois Nations, we build but one fire, and we have through all of time dwelt under one roof." (9)

The general features of The Iroquois Confederacy may be summarized in the following propositions: 1. The Confederacy was a union of Five Tribes, composed of common gentes, under one government on the basis of equality; each tribe remaining independent in all matters pertaining to local self-government. 2. It created a General Council of Sachems, who were limited in number, equal in rank and authority, and invested with supreme powers over all matters pertaining to the Confederacy. 3. Fifty Sachemships were created and named in perpetuity in certain gentes of the several tribes; with power in these gentes to fill vacancies, as often as they occurred, by election from among their respective members, and with the further power to depose from office for cause; but the right to invest these Sachems with office was reserved to the General Council. 4. The Sachems of the Confederacy were also Sachems in their respective Tribes, and with the Chiefs formed the Council of each, which was supreme over all matters pertaining to the Tribe exclusively. 5. Unanimity in the Council of the Confederacy was made essential to every public act. 6. In the General Council the Sachems voted by Tribes, which gave to each Tribe a negative upon the others. 7. The Council of each tribe had power to convene the General Council; but the later had no power to convene itself. 8. The General Council was open to the orators of the people for the discussion of public questions; but the

Council alone decided. 9. The Confederacy had no Chief Executive Magistrate, or official head. 10. Experiencing the necessity for a General Military Commander they created the office in a dual form, that one might neutralize the other. The two principal War-Chiefs created were made equal in powers. (10)

The Seats of Hiawatha and Deganawidah were never to be filled again. The name of each sachemship is also the personal name of each sachem while he holds the office, each one in succession taking the name of his predecessor.... They were all upon equality in rank, authority, and privileges... The Mohawks had nine sachems, the Oneidas nine, the Onondagas fourteen, the Cayugas ten, the Senecas eight. (11)

The 'Long House' (Hau-de-no-sote was made the symbol of the Confederacy; and they styled themselves the "People of The Long House" Hau-de-no-sau-nee). This was the name, and the only name, with which they distinguished themselves. (12)

The Constitution of The Iroquois League Reads as Follows:

"The Onondaga lords shall open each council by expressing their gratitude to their cousin lords, and greeting them, and they shall make an address and offer thanks to the earth where men dwell, to the streams of water, the pool, the springs, the lakes, to the maize and the fruits, to the medicinal herbs and the trees, to the forest trees for their usefulness, to the animals that serve as food and who offer their pelts as clothing, to the great winds and the lesser winds, to the Thunders, and the Sun, the mighty warrior, to the moon, to the messengers of the Great Spirit who dwells in the skies above, who give all things useful to men, who is the source and ruler of health and life. Then shall the Onondaga lords declare the Council open." (13)

Through the influence of Hiawatha and Deganawidah, The League of The Hau-De-No-Sau-Nee or Longhouse envisioned that other tribes-all tribes-other nations-in fact, ALL NATIONS of The Earth might in due time become part of The United Nations of The Iroquois. And today, not far from where Deganawidah received his Great Vision of The League of United Nations — The United Nations from all across the earth have become participants! And may God, The Great Spirit - The Giver of Breath - grant that soon All Nations of The Earth will become a Democracy and Participants in THE UNITED NATIONS! *(Edited by Chief Irving Powless, Jr., of the Onondaga Nation, he says they were known as the Hau-De-No-Sau-Nee and their leaders were not called Sachems.)*

CHARACTERISTICS OF THE AMERICAN INDIAN

In the first report of Christopher Columbus to his queen, Isabella, he reports on these new people that he has erroneously called Indians. He spoke of them as being generous almost to a fault. (1)

D'Arcy McNickle in They Came here First, reports that Columbus said, "After they have shaken off their fear of us, they display a liberality in their behavior which no one would believe without witnessing it. No request of anything from them is ever refused, but they rather invite acceptance of what they possess, and manifest such a generosity that they would give away their own hearts. Let the article be of great or small value, they offer it readily, and receive anything which is tendered in return with perfect content." (2)

Herman J. Viole in After Columbus - The Smithsonian Chronicle of The North American Indians reports Columbus saying, "They are affectionate people and without covetousness and apt for anything, which I certify, I believe there is no better people or land in the world. They love their neighbors as themselves and have the sweetest speech in the world and gentle, and are always smiling." (3)

Those who encountered the American Indian in their natural state and in a non-threatening circumstance seemed to find Columbus's description to be quite accurate and universal about The American Indian.

William Penn was very much impressed with the generosity of the Delawares. He said, "In Liberality they excel, nothing is too good for a Friend; .....(they are) light of Heart, (with) strong

Great Principles of The American Indian

Intensely Spiritual Culture - Permeates All.
Live in Harmony with All Things
Regarded The Earth as "Beloved Mother Earth."
Made use of what was available to meet his needs.
Evolved Great Love of "Freedom
In his natural state, he was a very good neighbor.
A "Disciplined People - A Society of Law, by The People.
Widely Practiced The Basics of Pure Democracy.

This beautiful illustration of Great Principles of The American Indian was prepared by Seth Rayburn of Fayette, Alabama.

Affections, ...the most merry Creatures that live, Feastest and Dance perpetually: they never want but little. . . if they are ignorant of our pleasures, they are also free from our Pains.... Their pleasure feeds them, I mean, their Hunting, Fishing, and Fowling, and this Table is spread every where: they eat twice a day, Morning and Evening: their seats and Table are the Ground." (4)

John Lawson in History of Carolina reports , what must have been almost universal custom among The American Indians: "Whensoever an aged man is speaking, none ever interrupt him, the company yielding a great deal of attention to his tale with a continued silence and an exact demeanor during the oration. Indeed, the Indians are a people that never interrupt one another in their discourse; no man so much as offering to open his mouth until the speaker has uttered his intent." (5)

I hold the view, and contend that The American Indian, in his natural state of being, prior to the impact of the white man, were a generous people. I believe this is the result of the widespread teaching of The Shaman, and The Spirituality of The American Indian.

But, more than teaching, this had become a way of life for The American Indian. I believe and contend that this can be validated by reading the report of Christopher Columbus, the writings of Captain John Smith, the reports and records of the leaders of The Pilgrims at Plymouth Rock, the leaders of the English Colony at Olde Charles Towne Landing, The Bienville Party while searching for a site for Mobile, and the experiences and writings of William Penn. And, I feel sure, there are many more such proofs.

Felix Cohen in an article, "Americanizing the White Man", in the American Scholar, writes that "In the Indian character resided a fierce individuality that rejected subjugation, together with a communalism that put the welfare of the whole family, tribe , or nation above that of individuals. It is out of a rich Indian democratic tradition that the distinctive political ideals of American life emerged. Universal suffrage for women as well as for men, the pattern of states within a state we call federalism, the habit of treating chiefs as servants of the people instead of as their masters. The insistence that the community must respect the diversity of man and the diversity of their dreams - all these things were part of the American way of life before Columbus landed. The darling passion of the American is liberty and that in its fullest extent; nor is it the original natives only to whom this passion is confined; our colonists sent thither seem to have imbibed the same principles." (6)

Truly, one of the outstanding tributes to, or outstanding of the characteristics of The American Indian is the "Good Neighborly" manner in which they welcomed the first waves of newcomers among them!

'THE PROFILE IN STONE OF THE INDIAN CHIEF'

In great excitement, she pointed out one of the greatest points of The Natural Bridge Park, in Alabama, and asked me, "What do you see?" Realizing that she was fully expecting a very specific answer I looked long and hard. She saw in my face, in my eyes, and in my hesitancy, in obvious disappointment, that I failed to see one of The Great Scenes for which this very Scenic Park was famous.

As an out, for this embarrassing moment, I told her that I would take a picture, and my camera would see what I did not see. Little did I truly expect what I would see, when I picked up my packet of pictures. I saw immediately, 'The Profile of The Chief'! I handed it to another person and asked them what they saw in the picture, and without a moment of hesitation, or coaching, she said, "It is a Profile of a Chief".

The Creator and Mother Nature had surely Created a Memorial to The Indian Chiefs of this Great Land, whose lives and leadership have led a People in 'Great and Noteworthy Achievements', that enrich each and all of our lives! Chiefs were chosen on the strength of the esteem of the people, and were challenged to serve the people without thought of or for themselves.

'THE LIVING PROFILE OF A CHIEF'

Stone Profile of a Chief in Natural Bridge Park, Alabama

As I stand looking at The Profile of a Chief - a Stone Profile on a bluff in The Natural Bridge Park in Alabama, I am reminded that there is a flesh and blood profile of The American Indian Chiefs.

There were many outstanding Chiefs among The Indian Tribes of this great land. The accounts that we can read today, point out quite clearly that those who were leaders - Chiefs - by the choosing of their people were noteworthy. In fact, many of the Indian Chiefs, like Chief Joseph and Chief Sitting Bull were spoken of, and written about, and dealt with by White leaders as though they were criminals. But, viewed and evaluated from the standpoint of the people they led and cared for, and on the basis of 'doing their duty by their people', they would be seen and evaluated as outstanding, and praised for being committed leaders to and for their people!

In America, in 1492, the author writes that, "In general, leaders were followed because they were generous, not because they could command or wield power. Good leaders took care of the people and, in return, received respect, allegiance, and support of their people. (1)

In This Country Was Ours, Cadwallader Colden in an article - The Iroquois Confederacy, 1727, writes that, "Their great men, both Sachems and Captains, are generally poorer than the common people for they effect to give away and distribute all the Presents or Plunder they get in their Treaties or in war, so as to leave nothing for themselves. There is not a Man in the Ministry of the Five Nations, who had gain'd his office, otherwise than by merit; there is not the least Salary, or any Sort of Profit, to any Office, to tempt the Covetous or Sordid; but, on the contrary, every unworthy Action is unavoidably attended with the Forfeiture of their Commission; for their Authority is only the Esteem of the People, and cease the Moment that Esteem is lost. Here we see the natural Origin of all Power and Authority among a free People, and whatever artificial power or Sovereignty any man may have acquired by the Laws and Constitution of a Country, his real Power will be ever much greater or less, in Proportion to the Esteem People have of him.

The Five Nations have such absolute Notions of Liberty, that they allow of no kind of Superiority of one over another, and banish all Servitude from their Territories. They never make any

Prisoner a Slave; considering how highly they value themselves above all others, this must be no small compliment. (2)

Leaders, or Chiefs were chosen on the basis of the strength of their inner spiritual power or orenda, and their commitment or dedication to the pursuit of Peace, and the welfare of their people. (3 & 4)

In Pennsylvania, the author writes that, "In the same way the Iroquois People to hear the words of Deganawidah, when they heard them repeated in the solemn ceremonies that accompanied the installation of Chiefs - words such as these: "This is to be of strong mind, O Chiefs: carry no anger and hold no grudges. Think not forever of yourselves, nor of your own generation. Think of continuing generations of our families, think of our grandchildren and of those yet unborn, whose faces are still coming from beneath the ground." (5)

In The Constitution of The Iroquois Nations - The Great Binding Law; Gayanashaggwa, the basis of a Chief is given: The Lords of The Confederacy of the Five Nations shall be mentors of the People for all time. The thickness of their skin shall be seven spans - which is to say that they shall be proof against anger, offensive actions and criticism. Their hearts shall be full of peace and good will and their minds filled with a yearning for the welfare of the people of the Confederacy. With endless patience they shall carry out their duty and their firmness shall be tempered with a tenderness for their people. Neither anger nor fury shall find lodgment in their minds and all their words and actions shall be marked by calm deliberation." (6)

The true 'Profile of a Chief' is best seen in such nobility of character, courage, and concern for the welfare of their people, as in the example: 1) the surrender of Chief 'Red Eagle' Weatherford to General Jackson, at Fort Toulouse, following their defeat at Horseshoe Bend in Alabama.

"One of the most picturesque and courageous scenes of the whole war took place here in the appearance and surrender of Chief 'Red Eagle', who had led the battle of Fort Mims, Calebee, and Holy Ground. 'Red Eagle' had come alone, accompanied by neither warriors or soldiers. I am sure that General Jackson was greatly surprised. According to Pickett, General Jackson upon seeing 'Red Eagle' ran from his marque and exclaimed, "How dare you, sir, to ride up to my tent, after having murdered women and children at Fort Mims?"

Weatherford replied, "General Jackson, I am not afraid of you. I fear no man, for I am a Creek Warrior. I have nothing to request in behalf of myself; you can kill me , if you desire. But I come to beg you to send for the women and children of the war party, who are now starving in the woods. Their fields and cribs have been destroyed by your people, who have driven them to the woods without an ear of corn. I hope that you will send out parties, who will safely conduct them here, in order that they may be fed. I exerted myself in vain to prevent the massacre of the women and children at Fort Mims. I am now done fighting. The 'Red Sticks' are nearly all killed. If I could fight you any longer, I would most heartily do so. Send for the women and children. They never did you any harm. But kill me, if the white people want it done."

"At this point, many persons present cried out, "Kill him! Kill him! Kill him! But, General Jackson commanded silence, and in an emphatic manner said, "Any man who would kill as brave a man as this would rob the dead!" Thus, his life was spared and Chief 'Red Eagle' took no more part in the war, except to encourage his warriors to surrender. He became a resident of Monroe County, where he operated a farm and gained the respect of his neighbors." (7)

'WILLIAM PENN - AMERICA'S GREAT ARCHITECT OF DEMOCRACY!'

The Story of Johnny Appleseed is one of the great Folk Tales of America. But one, far more complex and far reaching in its impact, is The Story of William Penn, who shaped and planted 'The Seed of a Nation'. The truth is, he helped to shape a Great Dream of a Free People - a Great Concept of a Democracy that would ultimately be shaped by the people, for the people. He has

William Penn

been called a 'Great Architect of Freedom'. Over a span of some half-century, William Penn - this giant of man in mind and spirit - gathered ideas and concepts and worked on, and shaped a great model of a new government - a Democracy. (1)

In 1657, when young Penn was 13, he was greatly influenced by Thomas Loe, an itinerant Quaker preacher that his father, Sir William Penn invited to preach in his home. Young Penn would begin to feel the importance of his life being guided by The Inner Light of The Quaker Faith. (2)

In 1660, When William was 16, his father, who felt he could now give him everything necessary to his fullest development, such as contacts with the most influential men of the day, and the best education in one of England's most ancient seats of learning - Oxford University. In Oxford, the eager, searching mind of young William was undoubtedly impacted by the philosophical ideas and proclamations of John Locke, about The American Indian's concept of 'government by consent of the governed'. It was the beginning of a growing respect for and appreciation of The American Indian that would continue, and blossom forth, for the rest of his life. He also came to the conviction that The American Indian were descendants of The Lost Tribe of Israel (a view held by James Adair, and others). (3)

While at Oxford University, William became a nonconformist, stopped attending the 'supposed to be compulsory', chapel services, and wrote about freedom of conscience, all of which resulted in him being expelled from the University. At this point in his life, he came under the influence of Moses Amyrant, and his Message of The Inner Light. Young Penn became convinced that liberty of conscience must be a first consideration in any well ordered state. On that principle, William would years later work to form and found a democracy in the colony of Pennsylvania. (4)

William became very much concerned about the harsh treatment of so many of the Quakers. The so-called Quaker Act made it a criminal offense for more than five Quakers to assemble "under pretense of worship". He would commit himself to helping them become free to follow their own conscience. This eventually led to taking all of them, he possibly could, to help him colonize his land grant in America. (5)

Thomas C. Cochran in Pennsylvania reports that, "so vigorously did Penn push their defense that the case became a 'cause Celebre', and in the end went to the highest court, where it brought a pronouncement from the Lord Chief Justice that a jury may not be punished for its verdict - William Penn would be remembered as one of the great 'architects of freedom.' (6)

In 1675, William Penn became a trustee of the New Jersey colony and helped work out The Concessions and Agreements that promised the colonists trial by jury, religious liberty, and democratic government, for as the document said, "We put the power in the people", and they recognized the rights of The Native Americans.

In 1680, William Penn petitioned the Privy Council for a grant of land in the New World. The colony was born on March 4, 1681 with the signing of the charter. (7)

Penn's purpose was to create a safe haven for the persecuted Quakers, and a place where guided by The Inner Light, he could experiment with government of the people, by the people, and find out whether or not it was good for the people. This brought into being Penn's First Frame of Government, but it was open to change and to perfecting. (8)

William Penn saw much of the kind of government he was trying to develop in the neighboring Delaware Tribe or Nation, of which he wrote, "Their Government is by Kings.... Every King hath his Council, and that consists of all the Old and Wise Men of his Nation (i.e., community), which perhaps is two hundred people; nothing of Moment is undertaken, be it War, Peace, Selling of Land or Traffick, without advising with them, and which is more, with the Young Men too." And later in 1682, Penn worked out a 'Treaty of Friendship' with Chief Tamany and The Delaware Nation which resulted in a peaceful, trade working relationship with The Delaware for some 50 years. He also had achieved a peaceful working relationship with The Iroquois Confederacy. (9), (9a)

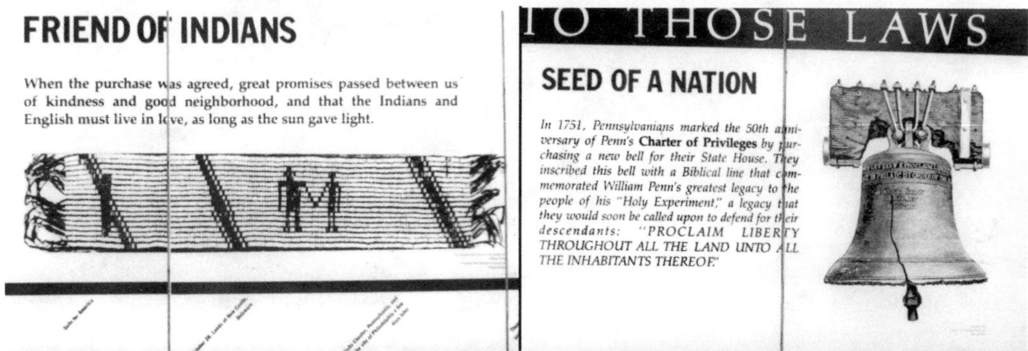

Part of famous Philadelphia billboard: 'Friends of Indians' (The Penn Wampum Belt) and Penn's Goal: 'Seed of a Nation'

In Through Indian Eyes, the author writes that, "William Penn, The First Governor of Pennsylvania, set an example of honest dealing when he drew up a Celebrated Peace Treaty with the Delaware leader Tammany in 1682, ushering in a half-century of trust between his Quaker colony and the local tribes." (10)

According to the Legend as told through The Great Treaty Wampum Belt, The Delaware Indians and William Penn pledged eternal friendship between the Quakers and The Delawares. (10a)

Of this, the author of The World of The American Indian of The National Geographic Society wrote, Peace and Friendship were oft proclaimed - and sometimes achieved." (11)

In a conference held at Conestoga, by Governor Gordon, with the Chiefs of several Indian tribes, in the year 1728, the Governor related to the Indians in nine articles, what he called the principal covenants of the leagues made with the Indians by William Penn and his Governors, which they doubted not had their origin in the great Treaty. (12)

The authors, Peter S. DuPonceau and J. Francis Fisher, in Memoir on the history of The Celebrated Treaty made by William Penn with The Indians Under The Elm Tree at Shackamaxon in the year 1682, write that, "The fame of the treaty under the Elm tree, or as it is called, the Great Treaty, is coextensive with the civilized world. So early as the middle of the Eighteenth Century, M. de Voltaire spoke of it as an historical fact, well known at that time. "William Penn, says he, "Began with making a league with the Americans, his neighbors. It is the only treaty between those nations and the Christians which was never sworn to and never broken." Other European writers have spoken of it, in terms of unqualified praise, to the honour of our illustrious Founder, and of the colony which he governed." (13)

Penn's Treaty with the Indians by Benjamin West.
The Pennsylvania Academy of Fine Arts, Philadelphia. Gift of Mrs. Sarah Harrison (The Joseph Harrison, Jr. Collection)

In a Pictorial history of The American Indian, Oliver La Farge writes that, "One of the most remarkable stories is that of the Delawares, who were the most powerful of all the Algonkian tribes. It was with them that William Penn made his famous treaty of peace when he founded Pennsylvania, and so long as Penn lived the treaty was kept." (14)

The authors of Memoir of William Penn's Treaty with The Indians, write that, "The true merit of William Penn, that in which he surpasses all the founders of empires whose names are recorded in ancient and modern history, is not in having made treaties with or purchased lands of the Indians, but in the honesty, the integrity, the strict justice with which he constantly treated the Aborigines of the land; in the fairness of all his dealings with them, in his faithful observance of his promises; in the ascendency which he acquired over their untutored minds; in the feelings of gratitude with which his conduct and his character inspired them." (15)

Truly, William Penn prayed with his very life that the colony he was founding would be 'the seed of a nation'. It is as though Governor William Penn chose to pass his mantle of 'Architect of a Democratic Nation' to his young friend, Benjamin Franklin - who did in fact, carry his mantle well! And I believe, that between the great work of William Penn, The Delaware Indians, and The Iroquois Confederacy Council, they provided Benjamin Franklin much grist for his mill. Indeed, they provided him much to chew on in the search for a 'Model for Union of The Thirteen Colonies in The Birth of The United States of America!

Penn Wampum Belt in The Museum of The American Indian, Heye Foundation

'TRIBUTE TO A GREAT MAN'

Father of a Nation - George Washington!

We all love to Celebrate Birthdays!

A noble life can be the source of needed inspiration in the midst of a desperate and almost hopeless struggle. Such was General George Washington to his suffering troops, holed up for the terrible winter of 1778 in Valley Forge.

The Prayer at Valley Forge. Gen. George Washington, winter 177 - 78. Copy of engraving by John C. McRae after Henry Brueckner, published 1866. (George Washington Bicentennial Commission

Some time ago, I walked through Valley Forge - remembering, and contemplating that experience, that sacrifice. As I walked around the compound at the headquarters, I imagined seeing a great and inspiring scene, of General George Washington kneeling in prayer in the snow. In his face and in his words, one could see, and feel and hear, his great concern for his desperately suffering troops, the great longing that their needs of shoes, warm clothing, and food might be met; but, most of all that they might hold on until they could win the war, and their freedom! Oh, the longing of the human spirit to be Free!

His great courage, strength, and commitment would indeed be a vital source of the inspiration that would enable the battered and bleeding Continental Army to hang on, to fight on, and finally to win the great struggle for Freedom!

What a man, what a leader, what a Father of America, what great courage and commitment; but, above all else, what a Victory he shared - in The Birth of America! Truly, 'First in War, First in Peace, First in the Hearts of his Countrymen! George Washington, we salute You!

'FOUNDING FATHERS OF AMERICA'

Staring

BENJAMIN FRANKLIN

There are many men who have helped bring forth the birth of America - a great Nation, under God, of Freedom and Opportunity for All! Several great ones among them are noble Native Americans - Deganawidah, Hiawatha, Canassatego, and Chief Tammany!

These Native Americans were influential, and respected as leaders of their People - Chieftains - who made great impact on Colonial leaders, such as William Penn, Thomas Jefferson, Benjamin Franklin, Thomas Paine, Charles Thomson, and George Washington. These were truly - Founding Fathers of The United States of America!

Surely, the giant among them was Benjamin Franklin, who made such a wide and varied contribution to the development of his beloved Country. As Paul A. W. Wallace in Pennsylvania-*Seed of a Nation* writes that, "Benjamin Franklin is the only man in Pennsylvania history who can be said to compare in stature with William Penn. Benjamin Franklin was a shrewd apostle of common sense. It would be tedious to discuss the Benjamin Franklin everyone knows: Franklin the printer, almanac-maker, newpaperman, magazine editor, book publisher, and pamphleteer; Franklin the founder of the American Philosophical Society and the Academy (forerunner of the University of Pennsylvania); organizer of Philadelphia's first street-cleaning and fire department; inventor of the Franklin stove and the lightning rod; architect of the thirteen steps to virtue, ambassador to France, president of the executive Council of Pennsylvania, and member of the Constitutional Convention. (1)

It seems the hand of God guided this young man, Benjamin Franklin, who was of exceptional and amazing strength of mind, spirit, and vision, into Philadelphia for 3 great and vital reasons: 1). To be under the profound influence and tutorship of William Penn, the GOD Gifted Architect of Democracy, 2). To be impacted by the amazing concepts and achievements of 2 great democratic Indian Nations or Confederacies of The Iroquois and The Delaware, 3). To become the leader of a Colonial Team that would do a search for a 'Model of Union for the Thirteen Colonies'.

The impact of William Penn on young Benjamin Franklin influenced him to become an outstanding student, of The Iroquois Confederacy or League of The Hau-De-No-Sau-Nee, for the remainder of his long and useful and productive life. He was, I believe, very much impressed by the words of Lt. Governor of The New York Colony, Cadwallader Colden, in The History of the Five Nations Depending on the Province of New York in America. Colden wrote, "Each Nation is an absolute Republick by its self, govern'd in all Public Affairs of War and Peace by the Sachems or Old Men, whose Authority and Power is gain'd by and consists wholly in the Opinion the Rest of the Nation have of their Wisdom and Integrity. They never execute their Resolutions by Compulsion or Force upon any of their people. Honour and Esteem are their Principal Rewards, as Shame and being Despised are their Punishments." (2)

The Town Crier - Selling pamphlets that stirred The American Revolution - much of it printed by Benjamin Franklin.

As a young printer, Benjamin Franklin became involved in printing, publishing, and distributing accounts of the meeting and deliberations of The Peace Councils of The Indian Nations. Franklin saw this as most important for the British Colonies to know the Indian leaders and Chiefs, to know their concepts and trade expectations, and to know the treaties they were making and with whom. This understanding of the Indian leaders, Chiefs, and Nations would be vital in order to establish and maintain peaceful and profitable trade relations. Though his first efforts in this were for trade benefits; as he sat in these Indian Councils and spent more and more time among the Indians, the Iroquois Councils in particular, he became increasingly more interested in their concepts of liberty, personal freedom and their concepts and styles of government - 'government by consent of the governed'. The views of William Penn about the Iroquois and Delaware ways of government by the people, greatly influenced this young printer to consider and study the ways and wisdom of The Iroquois Sachems in conducting the business of their Councils. Franklin became quite an excellent student of the Indian's culture and institutions. (4)

I feel sure, that Benjamin Franklin was greatly influenced by the writings of Thomas Moore's Utopia, John Locke and Jean Jacques Rousseau writings about observations of Native Americans on natural society, natural law, and natural rights. Felix S. Cohen in Americanizing The White Man writes that, "Out of America came the vision of a Utopia, where all men might be free, where government might rest upon the consent of the governed, rather than upon the divine rights of Kings, where no man could be dispossessed of the land he used for his sustenance." (6)

Through his writings, publishing of pamphlets, books, and magazines, and his work, contacts, and speeches, Benjamin Franklin became one of the most significant influences in the evolvement of The Enlightenment that swept over America and Europe, giving birth to egalitarian ideas and democracy.

In *Indian Givers*, Jack McIver Weatherford writes that, "Franklin became a lifelong champion of the Indian political structure, and advocated its use by the Americans." (6a) Bruce E. Johansen in *Forgotten Founders- How the American Indian Helped Shape Democracy*, writes that, "And from the earliest days of his professional life, Franklin was drawn to the diplomatic and ideological interchange of these councils - first as a printer of their proceedings, then as a Colonial envoy, the beginning of one of the most distinguished diplomatic careers in American history. Out of these councils grew an early campaign by Franklin for Colonial union on a federal model, very similar to the Iroquois system." I imagine that in this effort Franklin often spoke his views and convictions as in, "It would be a strange thing if Six Nations of ignorant savages should be capable of forming a scheme for such a union, and be able to execute it in such a manner, as that it has subsisted for ages, and appears indissoluble; and yet that a like union should be impracticable for ten or a dozen English colonies, to whom it is more necessary and must be more advantageous, and whom cannot be supposed to want an equal understanding of their interests." (7), (8)

In a Council of The Hau-De-No-Sau-Nee at Lancaster, Pennsylvania in 1744, Chief Canassatego suggested that the leaders of the English Colonies should consider forming a union and government like theirs, saying, "Our Wise forefathers established Union and Amity between the Five Nations. This has made us formidable; this has given us great Weight and Authority with our neighboring Nations. We are a powerful Confederacy; and by your observing the same methods, our Wise Forefathers have taken, you will acquire such Strengths and Power. Therefore whatever befall you, never fall out with one another." (11)

In the ensuing years after 1744, Benjamin Franklin became part of a team searching for a usable and workable model of union. The basic reason for this search was 1st, to create and maintain good working relations with the Indian Tribes and nations. And 2ndly, it was to enable them to establish self-government for the Colonies for their self interest and protection. Of this search, C. Fayne Porter in *Hiawatha, the Mohawk- Father of Our Constitution* writes that, "For a century and a half the colonists would live side by side with a people governed by a strict constitution; when it came time for them to make up a set of procedures of their own, where more logically could they look than to the Hau-de-no-sau-nee?" (10)

In 1754, Benjamin Franklin proposed a plan for a federal union of the 13 Colonies as a means of creating better, smoother, more agreeable and workable relations with the Indian Nations, with whom the colonies sought to trade. He and the team, who were working together to develop a model of federal union for the Colonies felt the time had come to establish such a union, and began shaping one from the bits and pieces of ideas from the Greeks, the Romans, the English, to blend with major ideas from The Iroquois League of The Hau-De-No-Sau-Nee. Of this, Jack Weatherford in *Indian Givers* writes that, "The modern notions of Democracy based on egalitarian principles and a federated government of overlapping powers arose from the unique blend of European and Indian political ideas and institutions along the Atlantic coast between 1607 and 1776." The Albany Congress approved Franklin's Plan of Union, but the Colonies rejected it, and so did The British and King George, who rejected the idea of appointing a president-general to head up such a union. (9) Out of his search for a model for Union, according to the author in *Through Indian Eyes*, "Franklin discovered a fine working example of representative democracy, with an unwritten constitution that spelled out checks and balances, rules of procedure, limits of power, and a stress on individual liberty." (13)

Benjamin Franklin must have been disappointed at the conclusion of the Albany Congress, that his Albany Plan of Federal Union for The Thirteen Colonies had been rejected by the colonies, and by King George too. But, it was to be a short lived disappointment, for very soon his loyalty to The British Crown began to fade away - entirely! And, in due time, he would become a strong and outspoken opponent of taxation, by The Crown, without representation of the people of the Colonies. Franklin became increasingly an advocate of rebellion against The Crown. He would use the colonists resistance to The Stamp Act to help stir up the flames of rebellion. I feel sure, that Benjamin Franklin came to a very strong conviction that the response to his Albany Plan of Federal Union had been a great blessing of Providence! And now, he committed himself fully, to pull out all the stops, with full steam ahead in writing, in speaking his convictions about personal freedoms, working for just causes of self-determination, publishing, etc. to the end of promoting rebellion and revolution. It was in this period, that he published significant pamphlets of Locke, Rousseau, Thomas Paine, Charles Thomson, and Thomas Jefferson. And, he used them mightily to stir up the frontiersmen on toward revolution. Jack Weatherford in *Indian Giver* writes that, "This Enlightenment grew as much from its roots in Indian culture as from any other source." (14) I believe it was the major influence toward rebellion and revolution.

Benjamin Franklin was so much impressed by the first pamphlet of Tom Paine, that he invited him to come to America and write more. He came, he became like Benjamin Franklin, a great student of The American Indian, especially The Iroquois, and in his pamphlet, *The Rights of Man*, Thomas Paine joined Benjamin Franklin as a significant force and influence stirring the colonist on toward rebellion and revolution against Great Britain. In *Pioneer America*, John R. Alden writes that, "In January 1776, Thomas Paine, who had come from England only fourteen months earlier, trenchantly and tellingly in his famous pamphlet *Common Sense*, urged that the time had come to part. Patriot of Patriots, Paine savagely attacked monarchy as an institution vicious in origin and wicked in practice." (15) Thomas Paine greatly impacted The Enlightenment through his pamphlet, *The Age of Reason*. (16)

As the rumblings of rebellion grew, Benjamin Franklin worked increasingly toward a Model of Federal Union for The Thirteen Colonies, based very much on The Iroquois Confederacy's Constitution - The Hau-De-No-Sau-Nee. As Carl Waldman in *Encyclopedia of Native American Tribes* writes, "The Founding Fathers of The United States who shaped the new democratic government after the American Revolution - people like George Washington, Thomas Jefferson, and Benjamin Franklin - used the Iroquois League as a model for the new democracy. The various states were like the different Iroquois tribes; the senators and congressmen were like the 50 Iroquois sachems, or chiefs, chosen as representatives or spokesman; and the president and his cabinet were like the honorary Pine Tree Sachems; and Washington, D. C., was like Onondaga, the main village of the Onondaga tribe, where The Great Council Fire burned continually and The Great Council was held every year." (17)

In the 1770's, Benjamin Franklin began to perfect his Albany Plan of Federal union, increasingly patterned after The Iroquois Constitution - The Hau-De-No-Sau-Nee. Benjamin Franklin saw that the Iroquois form of government derived its powers from the consent of the People, the governed - from and by the will of the PEOPLE! Alvin M, JOSEPHY, Jr., in 500 Nations writes that, "Benjamin Franklin, who had served as a Colonial Indian Commissioner and had met with Iroquois leaders, was inspired by the example of the League of the Hau-De-No-Sau-Nee. Although his plan for uniting the colonies, presented in 1754, was not adopted, it later influenced Franklin's draft of the Articles of Confederation of the new United States in 1777." (18)

In May, 1775, The Second Continental Congress met at Independence Hall, Philadelphia to wrestle with the issue of breaking with The mother Country - Great Britain. And July 2nd, 1776, they resolved that these United States are and of right ought to be free and independent states; that they are absolved from all allegiance to The British Crown, and that all political connection between them and the state of Great Britain, is and ought to be totally dissolved. (19) Benjamin Franklin was part of the committee that recommended The Great Seal, with its Eagle holding 13

Great Seal of The United States (Eagle holding 13 arrows in its claw, like The Iroquois Symbol that holds 6 representing the Six Nations of The Iroquois in The Confederacy.)

arrows, very much like The Iroquois Symbol with its Eagle holding 6 arrows for the Six Nations of The League of The Hau-De-No-Sau-Nee. In Symbols of The Nations, A, Guy Hope and Janet Barker Hope write that, "In its claws the eagle grasps a green laurel branch and a sheaf of silver arrows, symbolizing at once the national will for peace and determination in war. Its beak holds a golden scroll inscribed in black with the Latin motto E Pluribus Unum ("One Out of Many") describing the merger into an indivisible nation of formerly independent states joined only in a limited coalition to resist encroachment on their freedom..... the Founding Fathers thus expressed their vision of a world which could never be the same after the creation of a representative democracy dedicated to the principles of freedom, justice, and individual liberty." (20)

THOMAS JEFFERSON - *A FOUNDING FATHER OF THE UNITED STATES OF AMERICA*

Thomas Jefferson, the 3rd President of The United States, was, as a young man, a great student of The American Indian. In Notes on The State of Virginia, Thomas Jefferson described his careful excavation of prehistoric remains, the continent's first archeological "dig" worthy of the name. (1)

Philip Kopper in Smithsonian Book of North American Indians before the coming of the Europeans writes that, "Beginning with Thomas Jefferson, inquiry into questions of American Indian cultural history was put on a more systematic, and ultimately scientific basis." (2)

In association with, and probably very much under the influence of the much older Benjamin Franklin, young Thomas Jefferson became an indepth student of The Iroquois People and League of The Hau-De-No-Sau-Nee.

Thomas Jefferson seemed quite impressed with the Indian's religion. On an occasion, Thomas Jefferson was asked to compare the White man of the Philadelphia area and the Indian community relative to 'law and order', he said, there was no comparison. The Indian People lived by their 'unwritten law' and had virtually no crime among them. He felt their approach to government was far superior to that of the European People.

Thomas Jefferson, as a leader of Virginia, advocated the inter-marriage of poor Whites and Indians, as a way of bringing together the best qualities of both races as well as to establish peace. (3)

Bruce E. Johansen, in Forgotten Founders- How The American Indian Helped Shape Democracy, writes that, "To Jefferson, as well as Franklin, the Indians had what the colonists wanted: societies free of oppression and class stratification. Thomas Jefferson wanted to avoid a society dominated by an European type aristocracy. He wanted the people to have access to public education systems and believed thereby they could govern themselves effectively as The Iroquois People did in their League of The Hau-De-No-Sau-Nee." (4)

In Indians of The Southeast: then and Now, Jesse Burt and Robert B. Ferguson wrote that, "This lack of hereditary ruling classes among American Indians was admired by Benjamin Franklin and Thomas Jefferson when, in the 1770's, they were studying the ways in which men have organized their societies and governed themselves. (5)

Thomas Jefferson devised a plan for "civilizing" the Indians. He wanted them to don European-style clothing, attend school, and most importantly, abandon hunting in favor of farming. (6)

President Thomas Jefferson purchased The Louisiana Territory, in large part, most likely, as a means of developing an Indian Territory West of The Mississippi River to which Indians of The Colonial area might be moved. Charles Hudson, in The Southeastern Indians, writes that, "It was Thomas Jefferson, who professed to have the interest of the Indian at heart, who first devised a plan to move the Southeastern Indians out of the way. Jefferson explicitly set forth the plan of driving the Indians further and further west. His main strategy was to install "factories" (government trading posts) among the Indians, to (encourage or allow) them to fall into debt, and then to force them to cede land as a way of ridding themselves of the debt." (7)

Statue of Thomas Jefferson, and the county named in his honor after formation from land taken from The Creek Nation.

Thomas Jefferson advocated moving all Indians of The Colonial area to West of The Mississippi River, until they became accustomed to White men's ways. (8)

In Native American Testimony, the author writes that .... "Jefferson suggested that perhaps the Indian might be "safer" if relocated in this new territory (The Louisiana Territory). Over the next forty years, largely due to clamor from the citizens of Georgia, and the newly created states of Tennessee, Alabama, and Mississippi, this policy of removal would reign. Of all the treaties signed with the Indians, none had such anguishing consequences as the seventy six prescribing wholesale emigration as the final solution to the Indian problem - over a hundred thousand Native Americans would be deported west of "the Waters". (9)

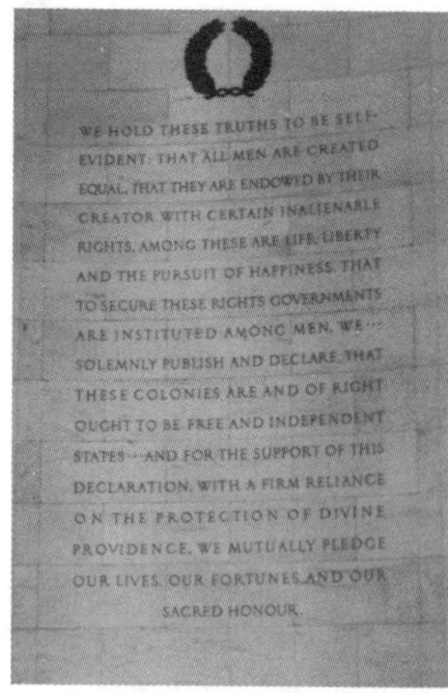

The Declaration of Independence authored by Thomas Jefferson.

Montesquieu, Rousseau, John Locke, and Thomas Paine were very much influenced by the concept - 'Government by consent of the governed', - or democracy that was practiced by numbers of Indian Nations, such as the Creek, Powahatan, Delaware, and Iroquois. They wrote pamphlets about the Indian's concepts of government that were printed by Benjamin Franklin and widely distributed among the Colonist. These pamphlets were also widely printed and distributed in England and France. In a Pictorial History of The American Indian, Oliver La Farge writes that, "The influence of the first observations on the Indian can be traced through the French philosophers to the English, and with it went the concept of, 'government by consent of the governed'." This idea was first put into specific words by the British philosopher, John Locke. Our own Thomas Jefferson, in turn, borrowed Locke's phrasing and used it, slightly changed, in The Declaration of Independence. The evidence is strong that the development of democracy in both Europe and America was affected by sixteenth and seventeenth century contacts with The American Indians." (10)

Thomas Jefferson, like Benjamin Franklin was very much impressed with Thomas Paine's writing, urged Paine to use his pen, rather than a sword - for 'The pen is mightier than the sword.'(11)

In The Columbia Viking Desk Encyclopedia, the author writes that, "He (Thomas Jefferson) had complete faith that a people enlightened by free education could under democratic-republican institutions govern themselves better than under any other system." (12)

Thomas Jefferson wrote these unpretentious words for his epitaph........ 'Here was buried Thomas Jefferson, Author of The Declaration of American Independence, of The Statute of Virginia for Religious Freedom, and Father of The University of Virginia." (13)

A NEW ERA OF HOPE IS DAWNING!

A distinctive Native American sound - haunting sound - the beat of a drum - called the group to order - the celebration of a new day of hope was under way. The dawning of that day at last was underway! What a joy to be present, and share this great moment in America's history.

A celebration full of Hope and Promise for a People long forgotten and too often passed over and passed by. The United States is at last preparing a fitting place of honor for our first Americans.

There was a wonderful affirmation in the Celebration - "We are still here!" I felt affirmed to, not because I am part Cherokee, but because I am endeavoring in my own way, for a quarter of a century to focus on the same goals as those declared here. The goal statement of the National Museum of the American Indian declared in the picture, therefore, I place this picture - Goal Statement - presented to me as one of over 250,000 charter members, donors, and supporters. You too can become a supporting member to help us reach these worthy goals, and join us in 2002 to Celebrate the opening of the National Museum of the American Indian. For further information contact - National Campaign Office - National Museum of the American Indian, P.O. Box 23473, Washington D.C. 20026-3473 or call 202-357-3164.

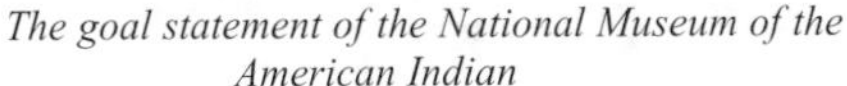
The goal statement of the National Museum of the American Indian

Model of the future home of the National Museum of the American Indian on the National Mall.

Next Page: Collage of scenes at groundbreaking for the National Museum of the American Indian on The Mall in front of The National Capitol, Washington D.C.

'GREAT MISSIONARY SUCCESS STORIES'

Methodism among The Cherokee Indians of The Southeast

I want to begin by looking at some of the background - something of who The American Indian are, and something of what The Christian Movement was doing among The Indian up to 1820.

1st, The American Indian as a People have made some amazing achievements. 1) They had learned to live successfully in every type area of this entire continent. 2) They had, in learning basic survival skills, also learned about many sources of food. 3) Thereby becoming the finest farmers on earth, in that day. A4) They had learned much about medicinal values in nature and shared it freely with their White neighbors. 5) They had developed a great concept of freedom-self-determination and of Egalitarianism-each person is equal and important. 6) Some, like the Iroquois Indians, had developed a government of the people, by the people, for the people and shared it - helping to birth democracies - The United States of America and others across the earth! 7) They had evolved a society in which Native Spirituality permeated virtually everything. The basics of that Spirituality was: Learn to Live in Harmony with The Great Spirit, Mother Earth, every living thing, and especially your fellowman. 8) They had developed great family strengths and values. (1)

We would do well to also remember that whatever The Church does is against the background of the attitudes, philosophy, and actions of the dominant White society. And there are some real problems here. 1st, there is little expressed concern to reach The Native American with The Gospel, from 1600-1800, there is almost no effort to draw them into any church fellowship or association. There were some, who seemed always to feel that The American Indian was not a legitimate concern of The Church. There were others who taught that it was God's intent that White man replace these wild savages, that the white man might properly use the land. The greed of White man to get the land of The American Indian, especially their fine cropland, was the most serious hindrance to any effective Mission efforts. There were those that excused the church by claiming that The Indian could not be reached by The Gospel Message.

Now, I want us to look at a great story of Mission work among The Indians in 1646. In The Harvard Classics: American Historical Documents, edited by Charles W. Eliot, they report on the work of John Elliot, a Congregationalist, who was the 1st, Protestant missionary of note to work among the Native Tribes. He was assigned as pastor to the church at Roxbury, among the Mayflower immigrants. He soon proposed to his congregation that he establish a mission among the coastal tribes. They agreed and became a sort of sponsoring agency of the mission. Eliot learned the language of the tribes he ministered to, and insisted on training leaders from among the tribal people to do the work of evangelism among their own people. In a report dated 1670, he said, "And while I live, my purpose is (by the grace of Christ assisting) to make it one of my chief cares and labors to teach them some of the liberal arts and sciences, and the way how to analyze, and lay out into particulars both the works and word of God; and how to communicate knowledge to others methodically and skillfully, and especially the Method of The Divinity," (2)

John Eliot saw his role among The Indians as being an evangelist, organizer, teacher, and trainer; but evangelism affected by the church would be done by the Native congregation and indigenous leaders. He learned the language of the Massachusetts Indians by taking into his home a Native. The unnamed Indian lived in Eliot's home and accompanied him on his visits to the Indians of the neighborhood. Later, when he preached to the Indians in their own language it was most effective and fruitful. In some 30 years among them, Eliot organized 14 towns of praying Indians, with a total membership of 4,000 Native American Christians. Each town was under the leadership of indigenous officers. A school was located in each town to provide academic and vocational training. This was a most Fruitful ministry - 'A Model Mission'. (3)

Had this type Mission work been done among The American Indian all across the Colonial area, the history of the church, and the relations between The American Indians and the Colonial People would have been vastly different and better! It seems to me, the way the Wampanoag Indians helped the Puritans and shared their food with them - the only way the Puritans could have survived - that they would have been filled with, and motivated by gratitude. This would have surely led to brotherly relations, but it did not!

My Granddaughter, Tara Leigh Phillips Long and her husband, Robert Long, Celebrating their 1st Wedding Anniversary in Savannah, Georgia, a city rich in Methodist Heritage.

Instead, the Puritans began feverishly seizing Indian lands without giving compensation. This of course caused conflict between them. Such greed for the Indian's land caused a low level of spiritual concern for and response to the Indian until in the 1800's.

John Wesley came to America in October, 1735, at the invitation of General Oglethorpe to be a missionary to the Georgia Colony and the Indians of the area. Wesley failed in his attempt to develop mission work among The Creek Indians. He did not use the methods of John Eliot. The Indians did not understand Wesley, and he did not understand them and their ways and their Native Spirituality, Wesley felt a failure, and determined to return to England.

Homer Noley, in The First White Frost writes that, "It was a flash of Gospel Light into the darkness of the eighteenth century - the principle worth all remembering - 'that it will be vain for us to offer heaven - if we grudge them a living upon their own land.' This attitude of course greatly hampered the work among The Indians." (4)

"Too often, as the missionaries offered a religion of love and eternal life, the colonists, on the other hand, were forming militia to kill tribal people or drive them from their homes in order to take their land and crops." (Roger Williams, William Penn, John Eliot, the Wesley Brothers, and such others were exceptions to such deplorable attitudes and practices.) "The newly established Methodist Church in America was finding its own way under the new government umbrella. Just less that one year after the Christmas Conference of 1785, Coke and Asbury met with President George Washington at Mount Vernon. At that meeting they sought Washington's support in bringing about the emancipation of slaves in Virginia."

"Washington declined to initiate personal support, but said he would express himself in favor of the move were it brought before the Assembly. Coke and Asbury met with Washington again, this time in 1789, just five years after The Christmas Conference. The purpose of this meeting was to express, 'The Methodist Church's support to the head of the new civil government,'

Apparently the two Methodist leaders (Bishops) missed an opportunity to express the concern of John Wesley for the 'progeny of Shem' - The American Indian." (5)

It is readily admitted by Methodist historians that the early Methodist leaders did not place Indian Ministries very high on their list of priorities. They do point out that at least some thought was given to the subject as - "strange to relate neither Coke nor Asbury felt deeply the obligation to organize systematic missionary work among the Indians." (6)

Historian Barclay in Early American Methodism: Missionary Motivation and Expansion notes that Bishop Coke wrote in his journal that they had on occasion been among the Cherokees and found them to be a peaceable people. In 1789, Bishop Asbury wrote in his journal that he wished to "send an extra preacher to the Waxsaws, to preach to the Catawba Indians in York and Lancaster Counties, South Carolina. Bishops Coke and Asbury apparently did preach to the Catawba themselves and apparently engaged in some preliminary discussion with the Catawba leaders about establishing a school in their midst. (7)

Homer Noley, my fellow historian of SEJANAM, writes that, "The eighteenth-century Great Awakening in the southern colonies is rendered meaningless by the continuous conflict of European nations, fighting over who would possess tribal lands, and tribal people, fighting to protect homes and families from frenzied, land-hungry colonists. Christianity could not prevent the uprooting of Native American families and the theft or destruction of their homes and crops. (8)

Then the threat of Removal began to cast its dark and grim shadow over The American Indian People East of The Mississippi River. Few felt this grim threat more, and over such a long and hard struggle than did The Cherokee People,

The courts and government of the colonies or 13 states declared the Indians uncivilized, wandering hunters who had no legal claim to any territory, thus, they were justified to drive them west of The Mississippi River. Roger Williams openly declared the Puritans were stealing the Indian's land. And therefore, he was driven out of Boston and Massachusetts. He bought land from Indian friends and founded Providence, Rhode Island. (9)

During the 1st, 35 years of American Methodism, The General Conference made no mention of Native American concerns; while making strong statements against slavery, they placed primary emphasis on providing ministry to the White immigrants who now were moving westward, often infringing on Indian land.

In 1815, in Marietta, Ohio an itinerant preacher was holding forth, preaching in a voice so loud and penetrating that it reached far beyond the building where they gathered. Halford E. Luccock and Paul Hutchinson in The Story of Methodism report that a Negro, John Stewart heard the sermon afar off and drew nigh. Stewart followed the voice, listened to the sermon, which reached his conscience, and as a result he was converted. The next Sunday, he joined the Church, and it was not long before he had resolved to go as a missionary to the Indians. He could read, and had a fine voice for singing. He first went to the Delaware Tribe on the Muskingum, then to upper Sandusky. It was not a jaunty camping trip he had undertaken, and he was frequently in danger of his life. He often saved his life by giving a vivid demonstration of the claim that, 'Music hath power to sooth the savage breast'. Among the wigwams of the Wyandotts he found a captive Negro, stolen as a child in Virginia, who became his interpreter. Stewart's work spread until he had the whole Wyandott clan under his influence. (10)

This work of Stewart awakened wide interest in the church and in 1819, The Ohio Conference adopted the mission and sent other missionaries to labor in the vineyard among the Indians.

In 1819, The Missionary and Bible Society of The Methodist Episcopal Church in America was organized. And in 1820, The General Conference approved and endorsed it. Also at this time - after long debate across the nation - The Indian Civilization Act was passed. (11) This Act made money available for Churches to begin schools among the Indians-to make the Indians more like White man-thus more acceptable among the White or dominant population (that was the theory).

In the spring of 1822, Richard Neely of The Tennessee Conference was sent to work as a junior pastor in the Jackson Circuit as part of The Huntsville District. There he met a Cherokee by the name of Richard Riley. William G. McLoughlin in Cherokees and Missionaries says Richard Riley was the son of Samuel Riley an official interpreter at the Cherokee Agency in the 1790's and early part of the nineteenth century, and a Cherokee woman. Richard Riley operated a business and plantation at Fort Deposit, near present-day Guntersville in Marshall County, Alabama. (12)

Richard Riley invited Richard Neely to come preach in his home. Neely crossed the Tennessee River, visited with the Riley family, and preached in their home. There also were other interested Cherokee families who attended that 1st, Service. The interest was such that Rev. Neely agreed to come once a month to continue to hold Services of Worship. Thus, began the famous Mission to The Cherokee according to Marion Elias Lazenby in History of Methodism in Alabama and West Florida. This was the 1st, Methodist Mission to The Cherokee in Alabama. (13)

There was no Conference action, no instruction from his presiding Elder, no authority from any Board of missions, but just the zeal, faith, courage, and wisdom of a twenty year old Methodist preacher - Richard Neely - who with the help of another preacher, Robert Boyd, then serving his first year in the Conference, as junior preacher on Limestone Circuit, held a revival in Riley's home in a Cherokee Village. The religious daring of these two youths brought forth great results. Neely soon organized a Church with 33 members, all Cherokees, and appointed Richard Riley its first class leader. (14)

The First official appointments to the Cherokee Indian Mission was Andrew Crawford, of The Huntsville District, of The Tennessee Conference, William McMahon the Presiding Elder. Judging by the views of William G. McLoughlin in Cherokees and Missionaries it seems that the Tennessee Conference may have been influenced by The Federal Government's Education Fund to establish a school among The Cherokees at Guntersville. Crawford met with the local chiefs, got their permission and opened the school at Riley's plantation, December 30, 1822. (15)

In a while, the Cherokee of the area had built a building for the use of the school. Crawford was to live among the Cherokee and teach and preach. He is described as a "Man of sterling worth, a man of education and of business qualities and habits, a minister of gifts and graces." He was welcomed by Richard Riley as a "bearer of Christian tidings." He reported that he had far more success preaching than he did in teaching the children.

On January 18th and 19th, 1823, Thomas Stringfield, pastor at Huntsville, substituting for McMahon, Presiding Elder, visited The Cherokee Mission and held a Quarterly Conference. There were several preachers present. The customary Love-Feast (Testimony Meeting) was held, and the Indians told, "in their own language the wonderful works of God." Three Indians were converted during the Sabbath Services. (16)

Henry Thompson Malone in Cherokees of The Old South - A People in Transition writes that, "The growth of Methodist Missions to The Cherokees was steady. In 1824, the work was expanded into the Upper and Lower Missions, directed by Nicholas D. Scales and Richard Neely. At the invitation of a Cherokee named William Coody, Scales' Upper Mission was established at Coody's home and farm near Ross' Post Office. According to William G. McLoughlin in Cherokees and Missionaries Coody was a White man that was married to the sister of the Chief, John Ross, (and living near him at Ross' Landing on the Tennessee River in present-day Chattanooga, TN.) Coody asked for a preacher to preach in his home in 1821, and was converted in 1822, and became the 'Class leader' for a group of Methodist Seekers who met regularly in his home for prayer and exhortation. The Indian also aided the mission by voluntarily contributing one hundred dollars annually. A year later this Upper Mission of The Cherokees had 81 Indian and 20 Negro members; while the Lower Mission boasted 108 Cherokees and 43 Negro members. In 1825, The Middle Mission was created, and Isaac W. Sullivan was named to its ministry. (17), (18)

The Conference had in the meanwhile become disturbed that in their zeal to convert Indians, the missionaries might fail to educate and civilize their charges. Bishop McKendree issued a warning in 1824, that preachers in the Indian Country were "neglecting intellectual and material instruction." Instead, he recommended that, "Guidance in agriculture and house wifery should be taught," Consequently, the assignments issued in 1825, specifically ordered Scales and Sullivan, first to teach, and then to preach. Richard Neely was allowed freedom to preach and operated from the two societies at Riley's and Coody's. M. E. Lazenby says of Neely's Cherokee Indian Circuit that most of it was in Alabama, though the entire Cherokee Nation was as an open door before him. And that he had not a rival or equal in all the field. There was nothing to arrest his march or circumscribe his operations from Wills Creek to within the chartered limits of North Carolina. He preached anywhere he could gather a congregation. (19)

In December, 1825, The Tennessee Conference answered a request from Cherokees near New Town (New Echota- The Cherokee Nation's Capitol in Georgia) by sending Francis Asbury Owens to begin a mission school. Richard Neely visited the school and praised the work of Owen and the interest of The Cherokees in the new Methodist Mission, (20)

Richard Neely adopted the life style of The Cherokee Indians, accepting them as his people, and married one of them, a Miss McNair, a Cherokee woman of education.

In 1826, the appointments for The Cherokee Mission were: New Town (New Echota, Ga.), Francis Asbury Owen; Gunter's, A. F. Driskill; Wills Valley, Richard Neely. In 1827, Neely broken in health, superannuated at The Annual Conference at Tuscumbia. Shortly before, he had preached his farewell sermon to the Cherokees, "Whom he loved as he loved his own soul, and for whom he expended his strength, exhausted his health, and had sacrificed his life." His last audible words were, "Heaven is a better place than this," In five years, he had burned himself out for Christ. (21)

In 1827, William McMahon of The Huntsville District was appointed District Superintendent of The Cherokee Missions. Francis Asbury Owen was re-appointed to Newtown; George W. Morris, to Gunter's, and William P. Nichols, to Coosewatte (in Georgia). These appointments were to schools. James J. Trott was appointed to Wills Valley Circuit, and Turtle Fields, a Cherokee was appointed to preach throughout The Cherokee Nation under William McMahon, Presiding Elder. (22)

In 1828, The Cherokee Phoenix, The Cherokee Nation Newspaper being now published at Echota , Georgia, their capitol, became a valuable tool of The Cherokee Methodist mission, as a means of making announcements of events and of spreading and communicating The Message.

The 1828 Cherokee Mission appointments were: Wills Valley, Greenberry Garrett; Oostaknahla, Turtle Fields,; Echota, James J. Trott; Ooithkellogee, G. T. Henderson; Creek Path, J. B. McFerrin; Chatooga, Allen F. Scruggs; Salakowa, Dickson C. McLeod. There were now seven appointments, manned by bright young men who became leaders in their Conference. All of these appointments grew out of the one started by Richard Neely and Richard Riley in Marshall County, Alabama. It was estimated that the population of The Cherokee Nation at this time was 15,000; and 700 of these were now members of The Methodist Episcopal Church, 345 of these in Alabama - (largely in the area of Sand Mountain!) During the year 1828, The Tennessee Conference collected $356.00 for Missions, of which two Missionary Societies in Alabama paid $121.00, Huntsville $61.00 and Courtland $60.00 (where I was born, 1930).

In 1829, James J. Trott, was assigned as missionary to travel all throughout The Cherokee nation. During the year, J. B. McFerrin persuaded Chief John Ross to join a Methodist Society.

And he was a great influence for The Methodist among his Cherokee People. The Newtown, Gunter's, and Wills Valley Circuits reported a membership of 675, with Wills Valley alone reporting 444. A total of $1,150.80 had been collected that year for Missions.

In 1830, there were now 5 schools and 5 circuits in The Cherokee Mission. Including a few interpreters, there were seventeen missionaries. At the close of 1830, there were 1,028 Indian members. Due to the great concern, influence, and commitment of Richard Neely and Richard Riley, the work was most effective and fruitful among The Cherokee People within Alabama. But now, a dark and foreboding cloud was gathering - a mighty storm was brewing and soon its fury would break forth upon the land!

In 1829, The State of Georgia passed an Act extending its jurisdiction to include Cherokee territory, and declaring null and void the government of The Cherokee Nation, along with all its laws. Civil and human rights of all Cherokee People were abolished, and The Cherokees were forbidden to continue working their gold mines in Georgia. (23)

The Tennessee Annual Conference, according to W. Crawford Barclay in Early American Methodism: Missionary Motivation and Expansion, 1796-1844, was unwilling to defend its missionaries among The Cherokee in their policy of civil disobedience, in siding with The Cherokee against the injustice of the Georgia Act. The Conference refused to hear resolutions that were supportive of The Cherokee People. Instead they attempted to distance themselves from the event: "As a body of Christian Ministers, we do not feel at liberty, nor are disposed to depart from the principles uniformly maintained by members and ministers of our Church in carefully refraining from all such interference in political affairs." (24)

In 1834, The Tennessee Conference transferred The Cherokee Indian Mission to The Holston Conference.

In 1837, there was reported at The Holston Conference that there were only 480 members in the three Cherokee Circuits of The Newtown District. In 1830, there had been almost that many in Wills Valley alone!

In 1838, there were none - The Cherokee Indians had been forcibly 'Remove' out of their Ancestral Homeland to West of The Mississippi River, by order of President Andrew Jackson, under The Army Command of General Winfield Scott. Though the tragic period - 'Trail of Tears' - occurred, many of The Cherokees who had become members of The Methodist Church, and were trained as Class Leaders, Exhorters, and Local Preachers, and Ordained Preachers prior to 'Removal' were of great influence in the new land — especially Chief John Ross, Turtle Fields, and Richard Riley.

SECTION TWO:
STORIES FOR THE CHILDREN

THIS SECTION IS DEDICATED TO THE LAMB'S MINISTRY OF REVEREND PAUL PROPST!

In the fall of 1951, The North Alabama Conference of The Methodist Church appointed me to the Belgreen Circuit. I moved with my wife, Frances, and our six months old son, John Michael, to Belgreen, Alabama, where we would live for the next three years. During that pastorate, I met a greatly beloved Pastor, Reverend Paul Propst, whose influence would greatly impact and alter my ministry for the next 40 years.

Reverend Propst, Pastor of The Saint James Methodist Church of Florence, Alabama, shared with me about his special ministry with children. He called it his,'Lamb's ministry'. I was deeply impressed with the great excitement Brother Paul felt in this ministry.

As I thought about what he had shared with me, I found myself getting more and more involved in similar ways of ministry. Across the 40 years that followed, I have invited the boys and girls in The Worship Services of my Church, to come forward, and I would share a story with them. The Stories in this Section 2 of this book are some of my favorite ones that have been part of this ministry.

The beautiful stained glass window of The Courtland United Methodist Church that I looked at many times from the inside in the 1930's while in the card class of Mrs. Collins.

THE PURPOSE OF THIS SECTION 2 OF THE BOOK :

I have written these Stories I Love To Tell for three reasons or purposes. 1st, I hope they will be helpful resources to pastors who want to share this kind of ministry with the children of their parish. 2ndly, I hope they will be a helpful resource for parents who want to share, 'Story Times'-bed time stories-with their children, as a way of bringing strength to their relationships, and of building family traditions and strong bonds of The Family Circle. 3rdly, I have written them for the sheer joy of sharing these, 'Stories I Love To Tell'.

CREATOR'S OF BEAUTY - BUILDERS OF DREAMS!

During the year 1958, I encountered an experience that would greatly impact my life. I went to see my District Superintendent, Dr. James E. Harris, about a problem (which I no longer remember what it was.), but, I do remember the serendipity encounter. I saw a side of my D. S. that I did not previously know - but, that would now change my life forever.

Dr. Harris was in the basement, when I arrived. When he came up, he was covered with saw dust. He was making a piece of furniture. I was captivated with the idea. He showed me lamps, tables, beds, etc. that he had made - that day a Dream was born in me, that is even stronger today - more than 40 years and many, many pieces of furniture later. Our retirement home is full of it, and I see pieces of it in homes of our family and loved ones! And, I still love to make it. In fact, I have several pieces started right now - will I ever finish? I don't know - Oh, well yes, I guess, when I go to The Father's House in The Eternal City of God!

Our Son, Danny Ross Phillips using the gift - Landscape Artistry - to beautify their home and grounds.

Open Letter to A Dear Son!

I heard the note of a 'Dream of Life', in our young son, - Danny - it was the Dream of Creating Beauty in the neighbor's yard. He was working at his 1st, job - taking care of some widow women's yards. He was taking such interest in his grass cutting job, that it was far more than just cutting grass, to get by and be paid.

At Gardendale, he got a job taking care of the city parks, while he was in high school. He loved it. He began to work on his Dream of making the Parks of The City of Gardendale, Special, Clean, and Beautiful. And the City loved it, they gave him help, and they gave him a budget to work with - and boy, he was off and running. And, his life was set! He would be a Creator of Beauty for the rest of his life.

He is currently, Creating Beauty at The Blount County Hospital in Oneonta(which joins Druid City Hospital in Tuscaloosa, and Medical Center East in Birmingham, as hospitals that he has beautified!)

Danny - The Dream was born in a little boy - but, it lives and thrives in a good man, son, father, and companion, and friend!

Open Letter to a Dear Daughter!

Laura, you have Dreamed from young years of living in Florida, and of Building a Dream of an Old Home that you could Love! And, today we share in the unfolding and blossoming forth of that Dream!

You and Pete had looked, no doubt many times, for job opportunities, that would make that Dream possible. The door never seemed to open. Of course, you know that down deep in our hearts, Your Mother and I hoped you would stay in the area, near us, in our growing old years.

But, the day came - the door opened, when both of you could take the job you then had - and take it to Florida!

And, to put the icing on the cake - you found the old home of your Dreams! One you could love - why, it was Love at 1st, sight! And, you have been working on it, shaping it to The Dream - and making good progress at it too.! One part of which was to develop - The Music Room.

We shared together, as a Family Circle, the Beauty and Great meaning of that very Special Room! John Michael wanted the whole Family to get together there, and we did, in August, and it was Great - Moments to Forever Remember - Sacred Moments to Treasure!

The Greatest part of it was The Sharing Time of Family Music. John Michael wanted to introduce The Family to a new, and budding musician - 'Jason and his guitar'. I thought it was a father's enthusiasm and special love of his only son - and that's alright, we will allow him that. But, Laura, you listened - and listened some more - and you said, "Mike, its better than you said." And, I thought you might have gotten caught up in the special nature of the occasion and gathering. But, no, we heard him some time later, at his home Church, St John United Methodist Church in Aiken, South Carolina, helping with the music for a 'Special Family Evening at Church'. And, I heard the leader tell Jason that he had done very good! And they wanted him to help with more. Of course, with Grandfatherly pride, I had already decided that he had indeed done great! And, he had learned it by himself, with the help of the Computer Internet - and practice and practice and more practice, and Sharing! That's how it's done!

'A MIND IS A TERRIBLE THING TO WASTE'

A Tribute to a Good Man - Booker T. Washington -lifting the Veil'

The human mind and spirit is a gift from God to be developed and used, for the betterment of mankind, and the Glory of God!

To lift the blinds from our eyes, or the eyes of any of God's children, can be a great and noble service. May God grant us the Wisdom to see, recognize and accept The Truth, and the Courage and Fortitude to declare it, and share it, that the eyes of all may be opened to The Truth of God!

Statue of Booker T. Washington lifting the veil of ignorance from the eyes of his people-Courtesy of The Tuskegee Institute

For the Beauty of the Earth
For the marvel of His handiwork
It is fitting that we
Praise and Bless His Name
Now and Forevermore!

Calligraphy-For the Beauty of the Earth, done by Margurite Busby.

'THE YOKE I WEAR ! '

In 1935, my Father, Joseph Robert Phillips, and I rode the train - the old Southern, huffing, puffing, smoking, iron-horse - to Glen, Mississippi, to visit my Grandparents, Mr. And Mrs. William Simmie Phillips. My Grandfather, met us at the train station, and carried us to his home in an ox-cart.

My Grandfather was familiar with the term - yoke of oxen - for they were widely used in his day. He was also familiar with the wooden yoke (as in the picture on the chancel rail, amidst the children), for I am sure that he had made many of them in his shop.

This symbol around my neck is called a 'Yoke', for it has to do with, 'The burden or responsibility of the preacher, to teach and proclaim The Word of God'.

This, 'Yoke Symbol I wear' is colored. This is of Liturgical significance or meaning, that is, it is purple in anticipation of The Coming of Royalty - The Lord of Life, or White as an emphasis on the Purity of the Life of The Lord Jesus, or Green which has to do with spiritual growth or Red as an emphasis on The Person and Work of The Holy Spirit in our lives. We are using it today as 'Green', because the main emphasis of the Spiritual Season has to do with growing in the likeness of Jesus. Our bodies, and our minds, and our spirits have God given potentials for Growth!

Children's Moment at Fayette First Methodist Church, using a borrowed 'yoke' to illustrate my 'yoke as a preacher.

Author enjoying the 'burden' of the pastoral yoke - Baptizing his twin Granddaughters, Shanon & Jennifer Phillips

Natural Stone Bridge Formations

'FOR THE BEAUTY OF THE EARTH'

Jason, my Grandson, smelling the roses - story I used with the Children's Moment that Sunday, at First United Methodist Church of Hamilton.

'Stop and Smell the Roses Along the Way.'

God has brought forth beauty in so many places. In many places there is great beauty that seems so natural - such as the scenes of the mountains, placid lakes, and dashing, tumbling, roaring, foaming, mountain streams! Then, from time to time, we find in unlikely places, those serendipities of life - great beauty in unexpected places. (I have included pictures of such in the book,) Rejoice! Enjoy! Give Thanks!

Such beauty, seems to tell us that God wants us to - 'Stop and smell the Roses along the Way'. Some sadly pass along the way, and never seem to see, and enjoy these blessed enrichments for our lives. Others stop and take a moment, to draw from these extras of life, that feed our soul and lift life to new heights, and then, go on renewed and refreshed! We would find our road of life easier, if we would learn to, 'Stop and Smell the Roses along the Way!'

One of those naturals is the 'Rose Path' along the lakeside at Lake Junaluska. It is very difficult for me to walk that path in a hurry, or in low-spirits. There are so many beautiful roses on that walk or path, that bid you to - 'Stop and Smell the Roses along the Way!'

Like a tree,
Planted by
The Rivers of water.

Calligraphy-Like a Tree, done by Margurite Busby.

'IN SEARCH OF CHAMPIONS'

We hiked the trails in search of Champions. One of the great joys of Mike's life was to say, "Come on Dad, let's take our 'walking sticks' and hike the trail in search of great 'Champion Trees." He found great joy in taking me to hike the "Sipsey Wilderness Trail", in the Black Warrior National Forest, and standing together, admiring 'The Alabama Champion Poplar Tree'. We enjoyed the waterfalls and the 'bluff shelters' in the area also. He loved to walk the tails in the area where he lived - in Neenah, Wisconsin - in Maryville, Tennessee (especially The Great Smokey Mountains) - in Aiken, South Carolina. We walked the trail along the old railroad bed in the 'Hitchcock Woods' - Mike loved this trail, in part because of the historic old railroad that ran through there, but most of all to admire the great and beautiful specimens of pine trees - there are many huge ones among them! He had a special love for the Aiken Serpentine Wall Park. He often took his Mother and I to walk through it again. We treasure the picture that I made of Mike sitting in front of a great "Live Oak" - whose limb spread was over 100 feet! (To him it was a Champion Tree.) It was beside the Serpentine Wall by Whiskey Road - a site he loved!

Mike and I hiked many of the trails that he loved - The Trail to Horseshoe Bend National Park, The Odum Trail across Cheaha Mountain, The Sipsey Wilderness Trail in the Black Warrior National Forest, The Tablerock Trail in South Carolina, The Trail from Davenport Gap to Gatlinburg, Tennessee, The Asbury Trail from Lake Junaluska into The Great Smokey Mountains, and especially many parts of The Appalachian Trail which were very special to John Michael Phillips The Boy Scout!

Alabama Champion Tree in Fayette, Alabama

Mike was very anxious that his Mother and I would make an Amtrak vacation trip to see some eight of our national parks (national treasures)! Part of that, was to

Jason and Marilyn Franklin (my niece and her husband) and Frances hugging a Champion Tree' in Glacier National Park, Montana

see the great champion trees - such as The Giant Sequoias of the The Sequoia National Park, and the giant redwoods of The Yosemite National Park - especially to see the General Sherman Tree! He loved hiking "The Great Trails" of our beloved country, and admiring the great champion trees - they had weathered the storms of life - and to him, they were majestic! On October 2, 1998, evening his search for champions ended - as John Michael Phillips received The Crown of Eternal Life!

Appreciation to Intertec Publishing, a Primedia Co., successor to Argus Publishing Co. for permission to use the Monarch Butterfly with this story of The Amazing Monarch.

THE AMAZING MONARCH

There are many great dramas that Mother Nature puts on - new leaves in the Springtime, blooming of the dogwood, the changing of the Fall colors, and the migration of the amazing Monarch Butterflies!

The butterfly on wing, so uniquely beautiful, represents the mysteries of life. In the Christian Faith, the butterfly is a symbol of our "Resurrection Life". As such, it is beautifully and symbolically used in stained glass windows, in churches and great Cathedrals. (1)

The distinctive color and pattern of the Monarch, beautiful though it be, is meant to be Mother Nature's message to butterfly predators. That message to these predators is like the skull and crossbones on a medicine bottle is to us. The Monarch feeds primarily on milkweed, at least milkweed is its favorite food. Thus, one of the ironies of life is that the beautiful and graceful Monarch that feeds on the milkweed (a pest plant by most) should itself be listed as a pest. In feeding on the milkweed the Monarch builds up a toxic in its body, that encourages birds and other predators to leave it alone. (Shane Ford in an article, "Mother Nature's Gallery", in Tom Mann's Junior Fisherman, tells of the Viceroy Butterfly mimicking the Monarch. In doing so, it probably avoids being eaten by birds. Birds do not eat Monarch Butterflies, because they taste bad. (2)

In September, Monarchs by the thousands, from across Canada and The United States, begin their incredible migration of up to 2,000 miles to their wintering grounds. They go to the southern tip of California, to Mexico, and to the Florida Keys, etc. How do they know when to go, where to go, and how to get there? We believe that they are guided by the hand of God. In Wings In the Meadow, the author, Jo Brewer, speaking of this amazing migration says, "The royal procession—the shower of gold—was a thing of the past, and no more was left in its wake to mark its passing than is left by the memory of a dream." (3)

In an article, "The Miracle of the Monarch", in Southern Living, the author says, "In no other form of life is there such a mass movement, such a stunning migration of the magnitude that take place among the Monarchs." The Mighty Hand of God that guides the Monarch, wants even more to guide us, each and all of us, in living good and meaningful lives! (4)

'PREACHING CAN EFFECT CHANGE'

John Wesley's
Rule for Christian Living
"Do all the good you can,
By all the means you can,
In all the ways you can,
In all the places you can,
At all the times you can,
To all the people you can,
As long as ever.....
You can!"

Calligraphy of John Wesley's Rule for Christian Living done by Margurite Busby.

It's no good, and no use, to be a preacher - is a feeling that has been shared and felt by many. In the decade of the 1960's, there began to be a widespread feeling of frustration among preachers caused by a growing conviction that preaching was not a significant medium of change. Many preachers were so influenced by this, that they changed to other professions, out of the desire to be in some ministry, by which they could help effect needed changes in society. There were many who came to feel that marches, boycotts, voter registration movements, etc., of the Civil Rights Movement were much more significant than preaching, and thus, neglected or left their preaching tasks to be so involved.

I saw value in many of the 'activist' efforts, but, continued to believe that 'Preaching is Ordained of God', as a most important medium of change. This had been confirmed for me in my very first year of preaching, in 1948-1949. I was just out of Lawrence County high School, and in my 1st, year at Athens College. I preached at a little rural Methodist Church in North Alabama, and as part of what I am sure was a very poor sermon, I said a Christian land owner should share the returns of the land with those who labored to make it. After the Worship Service, a widow, with very large land holdings invited me to dinner at her home. After the meal was finished, she asked me if I thought that sermon applied to her - and I nearly fell out of my chair. I was so stunned that it seemed an eternity before I could answer. I asked her what she thought, and she said, yes. We talked a moment or so more, and I excused myself, with needing to check on some matter - but, in truth, wanting to get out of a very uncomfortable situation.

Within some 10 days, she had had stacks of lumber placed by each of the many homes on her farms. And each was greatly improved. And, in some cases, these houses were well off the ground, not underpinned, and the floors had cracks between the boards that made it easy to see if there were any eggs to gather up, without having to crawl under the house and check each nest. But, it also made the house terribly cold in the bitter winter time. Many families 'Thanked God!' for that sermon. And some Black families came to hear me preach, and thank me too!

'THIS IS A SANCTUARY'

Some years ago - 1958 - I believe it was, our family drove into a parking-viewing area in The Great Smoky Mountains, and as I parked, I was confronted with a sign - "This is a Sanctuary". Now, with my training and commitment, the term sanctuary has one meaning - a place of Worship of God. And I had just come from Lexington, Alabama, where sanctuary had a very profound meaning - where some 75% of the members were in Church virtually every Sunday!

Sanctuary has several meanings. First, it means to me, a place Dedicated to The Worship of God. And, my thoughts go very easily to the beautiful Sanctuary on the corner of Military Road and Highway 278 East. Surely, most who enter would feel it is beautiful and fittingly appointed and kept. And, it evidences considerable love for its beauty and sacredness.

Now, I turned to Mr. Webster, to help me with this word - for it has several meanings. And, for a moment, my mind went back to a boyhood experience of standing by the desk of Mr. Webster, not while - but, where he did all this work for his dictionary. He says: 1) a place set aside for religious worship, as a church or temple. 2) The main room for services in a house of worship, 3) A place where one can find safety or shelter as (the criminals found sanctuary in a church). 4) A place where birds and animals are protected from hunters.

Trillium flowers in Glacier National Park.

Cascade Falls in The Great Smoky Mountains

Scenes on the bank of Buttahatchie River that inspired the message, 'This is a Sanctuary' that I used for a United Methodist Women's Meeting.

Now to be sure, that last one was the primary meaning of the sign in The Smoky Mountain parking lot - along with protecting the plants, flowers, rocks, etc,! But, even there, maybe I should say, especially there in those Magnolious Mountains, it had the higher meaning for me, for there I felt the nearness and Love of God! And Surely, I felt the deep longing to burst forth in singing - "Praise God from Whom all Blessings Flow!" (1), (2), (3)

And surely, here in this beautiful sanctuary, we feel the Beauty, Greatness, and Love of God!

This Sanctuary - Everywhere that we can experience God's Presence and Love - and can truly become The People of God!

'FOOD FOR THE SOUL'

There are many sources of food in nature - berries, nuts, fruit, roots, plants, etc. Many persons who have gone through 'survival training' have been amazed at the many things they found as potential food.

A Friend was carrying a group of boys and girls on a nature hike. He was pointing out many of the plants, etc. that were usable as food - such as, poke salad, water cress, hickory nuts, possum grapes, dandelions, pink root pig weed (of the Amaranths family), and maybe the acorns that can be used for bread, or eaten as nuts, and sassafras roots for a drink, etc. Someone asked him, "What is a flower-like this beautiful yellow of the dandelion - good for? What food is this?" And, my friend said, "It is food for the soul." A wise answer of a sage Elder!

Dandelion Blooms by the side of the road.

Many of you mothers and grandmothers have received some dandelion blooms as an expression of love from a little one! Maybe, dandelion blooms aren't normally your favorite flower, but, as such an offering of love - it is both beautiful and precious! How many moms have received a bitter-weed or dandelion bloom with 'Love' from your little one?

Aesop's Fables:

The Ant and the Grasshopper

One frosty autumn day an ant was busily storing away some of the kernels of wheat which he had gathered during the summer to tide him over the coming winter.

A grasshopper, half perishing from hunger, came limping by. Perceiving what the industrious ant was doing, he asked for a morsel from the ant's store to save his life.

"What were you doing all during the summer while I was busy harvesting?" inquired the ant. "Oh," replied the grasshopper, "I was not idle. I was singing and chirping all day long."

"Well," said the ant, smiling grimly as he locked his granary door, "Since you sang all summer, it looks as though you would have to dance all winter."

Application:

It is thrifty to prepare today for the wants of tomorrow.

Calligraphy - Aesop's Fables - The Ant and the Grasshopper, done by Margurite Busby.

Memorial Marker - Tribute to Jesse Owens, Memorial Park, Oakville, Alabama.

'THE OLYMPIC GAMES'

In ancient times, the Greeks held contest in racing, wrestling, jumping, and other athletics sports at the funeral of heroes of State. The Olympic Games began in Olympia, Greece in 776 B. C. These athletic games were held at the chief ancient Pan-Hellenic festival in honor of Zeus, one of the higher gods of Greek Mythology. 1) They were held every four years for over a thousand years. If any of the Greek people were at war, an armistice was called for the duration of the games. These contests also included drama, music, poetry, and oratory. The contestants came from all parts of Greece. The visitors received laurel wreaths or jars of oil, and won great fame for themselves and their native cities. In 1896, the idea of the Olympic Games was revived in Athens, Greece. It now draws world-side participation. (1), (2)

Statue of Jesse Owens and the Olympic Symbols in Memorial Park, Oakville, Alabama.

The current Olympic Games are very much in the news, world-wide. There are millions across the world watching by television as the young athletes compete, and rejoice with the winners.

In 1936, Jesse Owens, a Negro youth, born in the Oakville Community in Lawrence County, Alabama (as a neighbor of my father's family), entered the Olympic Games. He went to Berlin, Germany to compete in the Olympic Events. He wowed the whole world by winning four Gold Medals! He won Gold Medals in the 100 meter dash, the 200 meter races, the relay, and the broad jump! Adolph Hitler walked out on Jesse's broad jump, but, ironically, Jesse testified that it was Germany's own best hope to win the event, Luz Long, who inspired him to do his best! And, he won! (3)

After a furor over putting a monument to Jesse Owen on The Lawrence County Courthouse lawn, the good neighbors of the area created a park in Oakville, and placed the monument there as a tribute to a great athlete, and a good man!

The mercies
of the Lord
are fresh
every morning!

Calligraphy - The Mercies of the Lord are fresh every Morning - by Margurite Busby.

Rose Path at Lake Junaluska.

Memorial Marker of Tribute to Chief Junaluska

'LAKE JUNALUSKA'

Lake Junaluska is one of my most favorite places on earth! Truly, it is a gift of Love and Beauty from God!

I have longed for, worked for, and made opportunities to go to Lake Junaluska. Sometimes, it was to attend The Candler Camp Meeting - The 'Olde Time days of Methodist Camp Meeting!' It offered opportunities to hear some great leader of The Church, such as Bishop Gerald Kennedy, or a great 'Prophet of The Church', such as J. Wallace Hamilton; or to attend The Missions Conference, Workshop, or Leadership Training Events. Sometimes, it was essentially a 'Family Vacation', and we attended whatever was going on, as we wished.

Rose Path at Lake Junaluska.

Almost always my trips to Junaluska were 'Family Affairs', - I wanted my family to love Junaluska, as I loved her! We set up our tent one night, after the office was closed in Camp Adventure, under the apple tree and slept on apples - kinda rough! But, it builds memories! Later, we camped in our travel trailer (Phillips brand, for I built it.). Still later, we stayed in the Junaluska Apartments, or rented apartments. But, always with great Joy to be at Junaluska!

I am especially proud, that my beloved Church - The Methodist Church - named our Southeastern Jurisdictional Conference Center in honor of a great and noble Chief, Junaluska, of The Cherokee Nation!

The influence of this great Heritage at Lake Junaluska has meant much in my life and in my Ministry! I Thank God for it!

'BLOSSOMS - THE PROMISE OF GOOD THINGS TO COME!'

Picture of a great cobbler - Such as blackberry cobbler!

When I see a mass of blossoms of apples, peaches, blackberries, blueberries, and strawberries, etc., I not only see the beauty of the blooms; but, I see them as 'A Promise of Good Things to Come!.

My mind so very easily thinks ahead to the day, when the apples, peaches, blackberries, blueberries, strawberries, etc. are ready to gather and prepare a Family feast! - Fresh Fruit in Homemade ice cream, or cobblers - wow!

And my thought of blackberry cobbler makes it difficult to wait - but, Oh, the wait, though seemingly so long - is worth it, when you get there! Yeah!

Legend of the Dogwood

An old and beautiful legend has it that, at the time of the Crucifixion, the dogwood was comparable in size to the oak tree and other monarchs of the forest. Becouse of its firmness and strength it was selected as the timber for the cross, but to be put to such a cruel use greatly distressed the trees. Sensing this, the Crucified Jesus in his gentle pity for the sorrow and suffering of all said to it, "Because of sorrow and pity for My suffering never again will the dogwood grow large enough to be used as a gibbet. Henceforth it will be slender, bent and twisted and its blossoms will be in the form of a cross — two long and two short petals. In the center of the outer edge of each petal there will be nail prints - brown with rust and stained with red, and in the center of the flower will be a crown of thorns, and all who see this will remember."

Calligraphy - Legend of The Dogwood-by Margurite Busby.

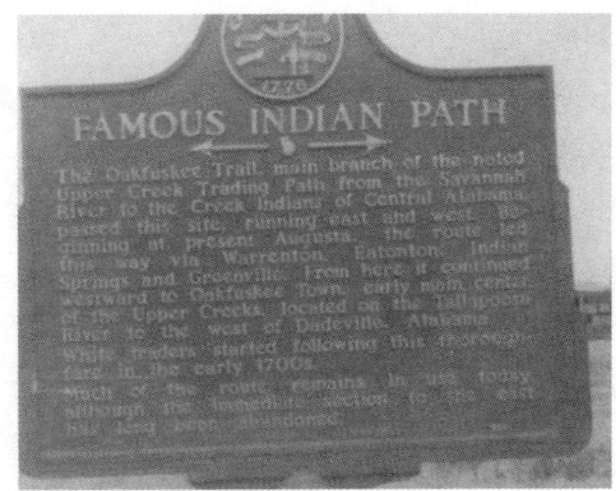

Famous Indian Path

'THE INDIAN'S WORLD IMPACTS SCOUTING!'

My first encounter of The Induction Ceremony of The Order of The Arrow was a very impressive experience. It was truly a Moment to savor and reflect on, time and time again!

The Setting for The Ritual of Induction of the candidates for The Order of The Arrow, seemed so much like I imagine The Great Council Fire of The Indian World, with eloquent oratory of Great Indian Chiefs or Sachems (Wise Elders of The Tribe or Nation). It was most impressive, with the glow of the great fire among the tall pines, along Wind Creek. (There could have been many times when 'Wise Elders of The Wind Clan might have done great oratory around 'The Great Council Fire', in that very setting!) The leaders of The Scout Ritual, in their Indian style Regalia, seemed as 'Great Chiefs and Warriors of the Past', admonishing the candidates to become men of inner strengths, and resolve, to be brave, to be very reflective, to be generous and sharing, to be caring, committed, and responsible persons.

John Michael Phillips and Craig Harris in a Boy Scout Fund Rasier for Cancer Research.

In pondering the Event, I wonder if the candidate for whom I was there, a fine young man from my congregation, and The Boy Scout Troop, sponsored by our Church, heard the echo of great orators of The Creek Nation from Ages Past - such as Chief Alexander McGillivray - admonishing young men to seek great 'Visions of Life', and to practice noble principles of life.

Was this part of the influence, that inspired and encouraged that young man to become one of the finest students - scholars - to pass through the hallowed halls of learning at Birmingham Southern College? And, to be much influenced by The Hippocratic Oath of serving his fellowman?

I also wonder, if a young student at Charleston, South Carolina, may have come to such a Setting of a Great Council Fire, in the days of The American Revolution, and heard great orators of his Mother's Wind Clan, and was influenced to reject the greed goals of wealth and power that his father set before him. Was he by such great and mighty orators of his Wind Clan's Wise Elders inspired to choose his Mother's Creek People as his People? Thus, and thereby, he made a choice and became a Leader of his Creek People, - a Great and Noble Chief of The Creek Confederacy - and to become known as The Talleyrand of Alabama and America!

My Grandson, Clint Blackman, with great optimism about to pull that heavy trailer!

'REMEMBER.....WHEN, THE IMPOSSIBLE WORKED'

Jerry Abbett reminded me of that day, when the shear pin was sheared by a stump under water, and the wind was blowing us - into the night and lost out in the lake. The day was far spent, the night was drawing nigh - and we were being blown across Lake Eufaula, toward the river and Georgia - and lost in the darkness of the night. Our little paddle was of no use in that high wind, and against that turbulent water - we were in trouble!

I looked in the boat, and in my tackle box for anything to make a shear pin - I found nothing! But then, my eyes spotted a little pencil - could it be possible - would a shear pin made from a pencil be strong enough to drive the boat through that rough, choppy, white capping lake, against that wind?

There was nothing else that seemed to offer any help or hope - no one in sight, no sound of a boat anywhere - so I tried the pencil. I whittled out a shear pin of soft wood - and it worked! The boat was moving very slowly into the wind - but, would it hold, could it possibly hold? I knew it wouldn't take much to break that little piece of wood, and we didn't have any more. It was our Hope - we just must go very slowly and very carefully. The propeller just must not hit anything! We almost held our breath, and prayed and prayed - and, after what seemed like an eternity - we arrived back at the dock, where our car was. It had worked! We made it! We were on our way home - in the blackness of the night!

My Grandson, Matthew Ross Phillips, about to knock a home run!

There are ways, and ways, and even unbelievable ways that will work! If at 1st, or the first way doesn't work - try, try again - it just might work. And, Thanks, be unto God, it worked!

'WE CAN MAKE IT!'

We climb a mountain - even a seemingly impossible one - one step at a time.

One of my favorite stories is of the little train engine, who said, 'I believe I can!' Though heavily loaded and facing a steep mountain, she believed she could make it, and she did!

I had gone with a group of Boy Scouts to hike The Appalachian Trail in The Great Smoky Mountains. We had gone into our third day of hiking, when we faced one of our most difficult challenges of the whole ordeal. It was late in the afternoon. It had been a hard and tiring day. Two of the scouts had badly blistered (sunburned from too long a celebration at the swimming pool, of being out of school.), places on their shoulders that had rubbed terribly raw. As we approached an extremely steep and rugged part of the trail, these boys stopped, and told me, almost in tears, that

Scenes of The Goodwater Scout Troop,Griffin Harris, Jr., Scout Master Hiking The Appalachian Trail in The Great Smokey Mountains.

they could not make it any further. Now, it seemed urgent to me, to get to the shelter, for the weather was very threatening, and they needed a good hot meal, and a good night's rest.

I helped them drop their packs and said let's rest and talk about it. We talked about the importance of getting to the shelter, and about the story of 'The Little Red Engine.' Then, I asked them if they could make one step, and they said sure. Then, I challenged them to think of our challenge, like playing a game - 'one step at a time'. And, they said, "Okey, we will try!"

We loaded up, and 'one step at a time', we slowly climbed that Mountain - like, the little train, I kept saying again and again - I believe we can, I believe we can! And, We did it! We made it!

'TABLES CAN TURN AND THEY DID!'

The clouds were hanging low, and oh, so very threatening, as we arrived at our shelter for the night. I was leading a group of some eight Boy Scouts, hiking ''The Appalachian Trail'' We were so tired, as we reached the shelter, and looked forward to a hot meal, and a good warm night's rest. But, it was not to be so, for we were turned away from the shelter, by a very rude and hostile man, who with a small hiking group had already established their camp for the night. We were scheduled by The Park Ranger, to share the shelter with them, and there should not have been any problem whatever.

Maybe, the man was very tired too, and felt the boys would disturb his rest. Anyway, deciding it was best to avoid trouble and possible hostilities, I asked our group of Scouts to sleep out in the woods, on the ground. It was threatening to be stormy - but, I reminded them we had trained to cover with our ponchos, in case of stormy weather. And, quite reluctantly, they did as I asked of them.

The next morning, though, the tables turned; for as we prepared our breakfast, a huge black bear came looking for food too. The bear

John Micheal and I hiking The Appalachian Trail in The Great Smoky Mountains.

decided that he wanted the food of the man, who had been so rude, the night before. The man foolishly grabbed a short stick - and hit at the bear! He should have never done such! He missed, for the bear flinched back, then lounged forward and slapped at the man, with his left paw. And, it looked to me as though those huge shining claws, just barely missed the man's throat. If the bear had hit him, I am sure he would have killed him with one blow - especially, if those razor like claws had slashed his throat or jugular vein! But, Thanks, be unto God - the bear missed his mark!

The Scouts and I grabbed our utensils and began furiously to beat them together - and to shout (as we had trained and planned to do) - and boy, the adrenaline was flowing! - And, it worked, it worked - for the bear turned and ran into the woods! We gave Thanks unto God! And, as we left the scene, the man - now, as white as a sheet - was still sitting and shaking - and never spoke a work of gratitude to the Scouts, for saving his life. But, oh, how proud I was of our Scouts, for truly, they had saved that man's life!

'TOUCHED FROM ACROSS HISTORY'

I have seen the Drama, "Unto These Hills", many times. It has been one of the most moving experiences of my life. I was most grateful to have the privilege of seeing it again, as part ofThe First Annual Convention of The Society for The Preservation of The American Indian Culture, in 1981.

One of the most touching moments of The Drama is when Tsali and his sons turn themselves in to General Winfield Scott's troops, in a noble effort to save their people - The Cherokee Indians - from further harassment by the soldiers.

All except the little boy is executed, by a firing squad of forced, fellow Cherokee Warriors. During, The Indian Arts and Crafts Fair at Eastwood Mall in Birmingham, which my group, The Society for The Preservation of The American Indian Culture sponsored, a little Indian girl ran to me, hugged my neck, and gave me a magazine. Moments later, I learned that the family of my dear Friend, of many years, and fellow laborer in The Lord, Tom Queen, was a descendant of that little boy! Thanks, be unto God, that little boy was spared!

'A BRAND PLUCKED FROM THE BURNING'

I am using a lighted pine knot as a symbol of John Wesley - 'Plucked from the Burning' - for the Children's Moment, at First United Methodist Church, Fayette, Alabama.

The rectory where Reverend Samuel Wesley and family lived caught on fire. Neighbors rushed in to help! Someone noticed that a little boy was trapped in an upstairs bedroom. The men formed a human pyramid or ladder, and a man whose name we do not know, nor will ever know in this life, pulled that little boy from the flames! That little boy was named 'John Wesley'.

He became known to many across the earth, especially in Methodist Churches and Circles, as, 'The Brand Plucked from the Burning', with compassion for people. His motto became, 'The World is My Parish'.

It is fitting that our United Methodist Symbol is 'The Cross and The Flame!' Surely, it is a worthy tribute to John Wesley, The Founder of The Methodist Church!

Tribute to a good man, Great Friend, and Faithful co-Laborer in the Work and Ministry of The Southeastern Jurisdictional Agency for Native American Ministries of The United Methodist Church (SEJANAM).

1. *This artistic likeness of Tom Queen, done by my Grandson, Jason Michael Phillips of Aiken, South Carolina.*
2. *Tom Queen, Director of The Methodist Mission in Cherokee, N.C., with the author on one of his trips into The North Alabama Conference to assist me in some mission - at Camp Sumatanga, in a District Mission Saturation Program, or in an Indian Craft Show at Eastwood Mall with The Society for The Preservation of The American Indian Culture, of which the author was a member.*
3. *Belinda Queen, Tom's Daughter, also came for the Camp week, and the Craft Show*
4. *James E. Manasco, commercial artist, skilled in logo graphics, showing the author the 'Will Thomas Memorial Tree', near the Corridor X. Jim is recording and preparing The History of Corridor X for The United States Congress. Jim is wearing the jacket of our long time dear Friend, Tom Queen, who has out-stripped us to 'The Father's House'. I have chosen to place this picture, that I treasure for many reasons, next to the illustration of Tom, the late Director of The Mission of The Cherokee United Methodist Church, Cherokee, North Carolina.*

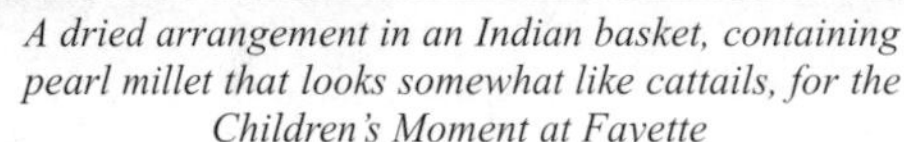

A dried arrangement in an Indian basket, containing pearl millet that looks somewhat like cattails, for the Children's Moment at Fayette

Pearl Millet growing on the side of the road.

'THERE'S A NEW KID ON THE BLOCK'

The phrase, 'there's a new kid on the block', brings to mind many kinds of stories. I remember the old man, who told me about his experience as a 'PK' - preacher's kid - and being the new boy in the community. Being a big overgrown kid, the other kids wanted to beat up on him, and he had to establish that he was tough.

One of my favorite stories, along that theme, is of the little girl, whose family had just moved into a predominantly Roman Catholic community in Ohio. One day, she came running in to her mother, all excited and exclaimed, "Oh, Mother, I am so glad that we moved here, we are not the largest family in town, anymore."

I have learned a new twist to that phrase - 'there is a new kid on the block'. Recently, I was driving into the Quad-Cities (Muscle Shoals, Florence, etc.) and was startled by a large field of grain that I had never seen before. It looked very much like cattails - but, I felt sure no farmer in his right mind would plant a large field in cattails. In fact, I pulled some on the road right of way, and later asked some friends what they were, and they said, that they were cattails. I found later, at the courthouse, from the county agent, that they were really - a new kid on the block - a new grain in our area. It was pearl millet. And now, often, I have some in my morning cereal - with Amaranth and Kumut. Great!

'BUILDING DREAMS AND CREATING BEAUTY'

As a young pastor, I needed a counselor to help me with a task that I was given to do. I turned to Dr. Hobson Clark, as one who knew the area of my concern. He responded with such a gracious spirit. Across the years following, I turned to him many times in planning Epworth Training Institutes, and in finding the needed leadership. He always responded so beautifully, and helpfully. I came to love and greatly appreciate him and his ministry of love.

Years later, in helping a dear Friend, Reverend Julius W. Vickers, Sr. ('Vic'), in a revival at Memorial Drive in Decatur, Alabama, I saw a different side of Dr. Clark. I found him to be a 'Creator of Beauty' - in other ways than 'Ministries of Love'. He loved to work with wood, and cutting and polishing rocks. The thing I was most impressed with was the scenes and legends on the pilasters in their living room. That day, I saw Dr. Hobson Clark as truly a 'Creator of Beauty' in many ways. How I wish I had a picture of each of those 'Twelve Scenes' - with Dr. Clark showing them to me, and telling me his stories with them!

In 1956, Reverend James E. Harris became a part of my life. He was appointed the District Superintendent of The Florence District of The North Alabama Conference of The Methodist

I built this entertainment center, facia part in particular, largely from an old cow barn that I bought and took down in the city of Hamilton, Alabama, while I was a pastor there. In a real sense it was an antique when I finished it and got it in place in 2000.

Church. I came to a great appreciation of Brother Harris, as an excellent preacher and Bible scholar. He was a gentle man, of a warm and beautiful spirit.

He had serious difficulties in hearing. On several occasions, he shared with me, his loneliness, and how deeply he missed having his own congregation, especially, at Christmas and Easter.

One day, in visiting Dr. Harris at the district parsonage, I saw him in a way, that I did not know, but certainly appreciated. He was in the basement doing woodwork. When, Mrs. Ellen Harris went for him, he was covered with sawdust and shavings. How, I remember that day, as they showed me lamps, tables, and bedroom suites that Dr. Harris had made with his hands.

The inspiration of that day had much to do with me starting to work on my dream of building pieces of furniture for our home, and for our loved ones! But, as I look back today, how I wish that I might have watched him, at work in his shop!

Even more, I have wished many times, that I might have watched my Paternal Grandfather, William Simmie Phillips, at work in his shop. I would love to see him making an olde timey straight chair, and cane it, or put a white oak split bottom in it. Of course, I would want to watch him split up a small log of white oak and make splits, put them in the trench in the wet sand, by the little creek, down below the work shop. I would like to see him take some of the soaked soft splits and work them down and soften them, and make them pliable for splitting or bottoming the chair seat. And, oh, how I wish for a chair for a pattern, to make one like it in my shop!

Black walnut Deacon's Bench I built for our Retirement Home.

I built this hutch from white oak given to me because of the time that I was giving to schools to tell 'Stories I Love to Tell', in appreciation by a man who spoke with pride of his family's Indian Heritage!

'SIMPLE DELIGHTS THAT WARM THE SOUL'

One of my favorite foods is a bowl of homemade soup. I cherish coming home on a cold, rainy day to a big pot of potato and onion soup, with hot, crispy cornbread!

Recently, I was visiting with some friends, Griffin, Jr. and Betty Harris. What a joy to visit with them and talk over old times together! I loved riding across the pastureland, over the beautiful rolling hills, and among the cattle. It was an interesting and exciting experience to rub and pat the monstrous size Devon bull. And, even though Griffin, Jr. assured me that it was perfectly safe, I was not very confident. For you see, my boyhood experience had been with a high bred Jersey bull from the Glendale Farm stock of fine Jerseys, and they were extremely dangerous. But, the highlight of the day came, when, at the close of the day, Betty sat us down to a delightful meal of 'country-style' (back home-Mama style!) homemade vegetable soup and corn bread! The fitting dessert was hot, buttered, cornbread and Sand Mountain Sorghum! Betty and Griffin, Jr., dear Friends, Thank you for a time of Joy and Blessed Memories!

'Sing Out Valley' in Concert at the Grand opening of
The Lanier Mill of West Point-Pepperell Co. In the Chattahoochee Valley.

'NOTES ON "SING OUT VALLEY"

Organized in early 1967, as a result of a performance by 'Sing out Georgia'. Twelve high schoolers began recruiting young folks from all area high schools, who had an above average interest in God and Country. The late 60's saw young people all over America protesting against one thing or another. It was the intention of these young people to be for something: the heritage and spirit that has truly made our Country great, and to 'pass it on' to anyone who would listen in songs and actions.

Sing Out Valley's first performance (They all began with the National Anthem and ended with, 'Which Way, America?) was on May 9, 1967. Their program gained popularity and was soon in demand. By November of 1967, the group numbered 200, with a 14 piece band for accompaniment. Rehearsal was held every Sunday afternoon and twice weekly during the summer months. The Director for the group was Dennis Carter, a 17 year old Junior in Lanett high School, who had unusual talent, musically and otherwise. The group had strong support from parents and the clergy. They were invited to perform at the opening of the Talladega International Raceway, having

performed twice at the Daytona Raceway and in Orlando and Cypress Gardens. The group also traveled to many towns close to the Valley and to Atlanta and Charlotte. They sponsored two appearances of Paul Harvey, nationally known news commentator and columnist, to the Valley area. A smaller group of 20 was formed from the 'Sing Out Valley' group to perform at churches, civic clubs, etc., where space was limited. They were known as 'The Good Neighbors'. At one time, "SING Out Valley", was one of the largest groups of its kind in America.
"Sing Out Valley" gave its 47th, and final performance on December 21, 1969.
(Courtesy of Bill Gilbert, Friend, Supporter, and Advisor of "Sing Out Valley", throughout its life.) (Credit and appreciation to The Pepsi 400 and the International Speedway Corporation 1801 W. International Speedway blvd., Daytona Beach, Florida 32114.)

'DREAMS CAN COME TRUE!'
GREAT DREAMS FOR SING OUT VALLEY BECAME REALITY!

In 1966, I met in The Valley (Chattahoochee Valley) Chamber of Commerce, with 12 high school youth, who shared a fantastic Dream. At first, I felt that I must burst that bubble, that they not be terribly shaken and frustrated by failure down the road. Their Dream of a Valley-wide 'Sing Out Valley' youth group to do programs and concerts, all over the country, seemed absolutely impossible. But, I could not bring myself to shatter their worthy, meritorious Dream.

They immediately were faced with an impossible obstacle - where to meet? If they could find a store front place large enough for the chorus and the ensemble, they could not pay for it, they had no money. And then, they knew they probably couldn't get anyone to let them rent or use a building or room for an 'Open Group'. Where could they turn? I invited them to begin in the Church - The Shawmut Methodist Church - where I was the Pastor, knowing full well the threat of such. The Pastor of the largest church in town, who was opposed to the 'Open Group' - including Blacks-came and warned me that I would be driven out of the Chattahoochee Valley.

The youth came, and week by week on Sunday afternoon they came - youth and their parents - White, Black, of Oriental descent, and of American Indian descent. And, they obviously were caught up with a great, and fantastic Dream - and I loved it, but, felt deeply their ultimate Dream is impossible, and feared it would yet mock them.

When, The Lanier Mills of The West Point Pepperell Co. had their Celebration of the New Mill with 'Open House', they invited 'Sing Out Valley', to do a Concert - Glory! And, that day - as I watched with 'Fatherly Pride', I knew, in my heart, that somehow, someway, by The Grace of God- and the support of good People of The Chattahoochee Valley - The Dream of those wonderful Youth of The Valley would come true!

The fulfillment came - (which I Saw from afar, because of The Methodist Appointive System) - as they sang such songs as "Which Way America", "Freedom isn't Free", and "America", etc., for The Nation at The Daytona 500, and The Talladega 500 Raceways - and, I was invited by Bill France to be his special guest, as Chaplain of the group!

A Dream - fantastic, yes-absurd, it seemed so - but, it became a Reality! DREAMS CAN COME TRUE, SOME DO, AND THIS ONE SURELY DID1

'AMARANTH - SUPER GRAIN OF THE AMERICAN INDIAN'

I encountered the story of Amaranth in doing research to write about The American Indian of The Southeast. My first intentions was to lay it aside and forget it - not so - I could not forget it - it haunted me!

I wrote to Auburn University Department of Agriculture for some answers, to some of my questions. They wrote me that they could not answer, how these primitive people could have possibly made the great achievements in agriculture that they had, especially hybridizing Amaranth.

The author looking over his Amaranth plants in the garden at Hamilton. The seed had been provided by Dr. Robert Rodale as part of a nation-wide research project on Amaranth.

Benjo, a Bolivian Methodist Preacher, District Superintendent of the Alto Beni District in Bolivia, and Director of Cenatec is working with an Amaranth Project with Ken and Sara Corson, Directors of SIFAT, Appropriate Technology at Wedowee, Alabama as part of the solution of world hunger.

They suggested that I write Dr. Robert Rodale of Emmaus Gardens in Pennsylvania.

I did, and he sent me material, that helped answer many of my questions. He also, told me that a Research Team had found seeds of those amazing 'Golden Grain Amaranth', that had been the food basis of The Great Inca Empire, that the forces of Cortez had intended to destroy from the face of the earth. Then, he challenged me to join his team in doing research on this potential source of relieving so much of the world's hunger or undernourished problem.

My efforts of assisting in Dr. Rodale's extensive research on these amazing plants was hindered by an improper move (part of the flaws of the itinerate system). It was also colored by the Sheriff's visit, on a caller's insistence that he check the Methodist preacher's drug weed garden. The Sheriff, my friend, got quite a laugh at what he found

Dr. Rodale's last letter, before his untimely death, was a Triumphant Report, that he believed had hailed the beginning of a new era for food production, in which Amaranth would be a World Super Grain, a possible solution of much of the world's starvation problem, and a great opportunity for all people to have access to this great source of amino acid, so vital to the human body making the best use of the nutrition it takes in! It has also been a source of fiber that has solved a major problem for me! Thanks, be unto God!

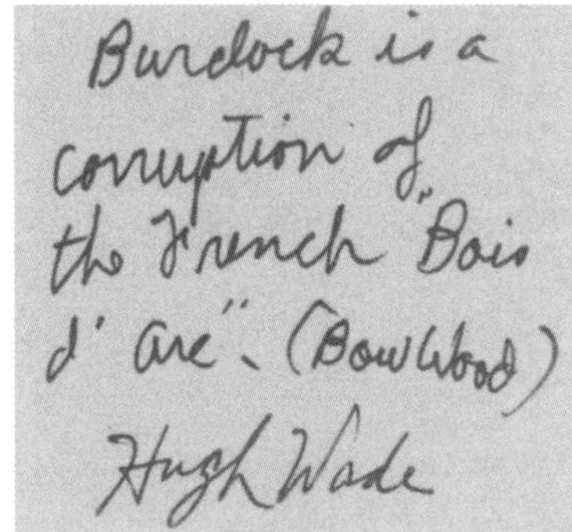

Burdock is a
corruption of
the French "Bois
d' arc". (BowWood)
Hugh Wade

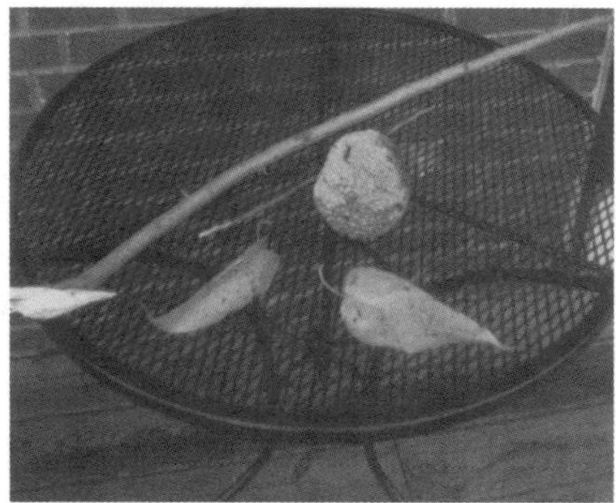

Burdock is a corruption of the French "Bois d'arc" - (Bow Wood) note from Hugh Wade

'HEDGE APPLES'-OSAGE ORANGE - BOIS-D-ARC'

I have heard the term, 'Hedge Apples', all my life. They are not real apples. That is, they are not like regular apples - good to eat and better- to make 'fried apple pies' out of. In fact, I don't know of anything that eats them, nor of anything they are good for, and I have tried to find out for many, many years!

There are few things on earth that are 'good for nothing'. In fact, there are none, as I see it, God made everything for a purpose. In talking about the hedge apple on one occasion, a man in the congregation, told me that he grew up near The Blackfoot Indians, and that they used the wood from this tree for bows. He said, the so called hedge apple tree was really the burdock tree. He also said, or more accurately, he wrote that 'burdock is a corruption of the French term Bois-D-Arc", Hugh Wade, Hamilton, Alabama.

When Hugh Wade heard me tell this story to the children at church, he wrote me a note, which he handed me after the Worship Service was over, that, "Burdock is a corruption of the French, 'Bois-d-Arc' - meaning wood of the bow. (7-11-1982)

Bust of Chief Seattle for whom the city of Seattle, Washington is named.

'MY WORD IS MY BOND'

As a boy, going some where with my father was very special. I hold many of those experiences as precious memories - fishing trips, hunting, train trips, going to town on a wagon load or bale of cotton, or much better, in the pick up truck for supplies from the feed and seed store, etc.

The one that stands out in my mind and heart the most, is the trip to the bank, with my Father. As a sharecropper, my father borrowed money each year to make a crop - to buy fertilizer, seed, and supplies, including enough food not on hand, or in the crib, potato bin, or flour barrel, etc. In the later part of the great depression, my father went to take care of his note, and let me go with him. As I sat by my father, he told the banker that when he sold his share of the crops, there wasn't enough to pay the note, that he owed the bank. Then, he asked if he must sell the cows, hogs, corn in the crib, etc., with which he needed to feed his family.

The banker said no, he must keep that to take care of his family, that he had known my father for years, and he had heard him say many times, "My word is my Bond." He knew my father would pay every penny owed the bank. And, he did!

I was so proud of My Father, I felt he stood tall as a good, honest, and trustworthy man. And, I must have stood ten feet tall that day! I have treasured that he taught me that worthy philosophy of life!

Beautiful Harvest Display of the Gatlinburg area.

' A GIFT OF COLOR'

One of my loves is walking through Arts and Crafts Fairs. Recently, in walking through one at Century Plaza, in Birmingham. I saw a beautiful creation - a wooden tulip patch. It stirred an image in my mind, quite different to what that one was, and I could hardly wait to get to my shop and work on that idea-image.

When, I made it and painted it, I liked it. And always such moves me to want to make one for many of those I love, who might like one too.

The rich colors that I used reminded me of an experience of several years ago. The night of the first football game after Anniston high School was integrated, a number of Black folk were sitting behind me. One of them exclaimed, when the band came out on the field, "It's about time they get some color in that band!"

Watermelon

Ice cream freezer

'IN THE GOOD OLDE SUMMER TIME'

Oh, the joys of summer-time! What are the special joys of the good old Summer time for you?

Birds singing, waking us, O, so early in the morning! April showers, and maybe, walking in the rain!

Oh', the joy of juicy, sweet watermelon, with the juice running down your chin. And the freshly made 'homemade peach ice cream', or maybe some freshly picked ripe strawberries in homemade ice cream, or even some juicy ripe peaches made into a wonderful homemade cobbler pie! - Yum! Yum! How much can you bear at any one time!

Maybe, just best of all - especially, if you are a boy - while walking in the April Shower - you let that good soft mud ooze up between your toes! Boy, oh boy, oh boy - how great the good olde Summer Time!

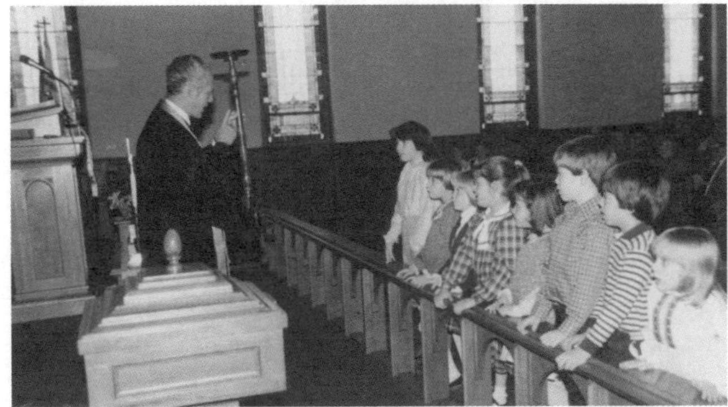

I am using a black walnut fern stand I built from a brush pile as a basis of a story for the Children's Moment at First United Methodist Church, Hamilton, Alabama.

'BEAUTY FROM A BRUSH PILE'

One day while driving across the Langdale community, I saw a man pushing up a brush pile to burn it - and rushed to stop him.

The sight haunted me - not simply the fact that it was a brush pile, or that it was about to be burned. But, that I saw in it potential beauty. I saw or envisioned the possibility of a walnut fern stand, from that brush pile.

I called Bruce Gray, Department Head of West Point Pepperrell, and asked if I might have that brush pile - at least part of it. He must have thought his pastor crazy, until I made him understand that there was a walnut tree in those trees that the storm had blown down. And, it too was about to be burned. He granted me permission to get all of it I wished.

This fern stand was made from limbs of that 'Brush Pile'!

The Liberty Bell (National Treasure and symbolic parable) - with its awful flaw or crack - as it appeared in Independence Hall, Philadelphia, Pa. and as it stands today in Liberty Park, across from Independence Hall.

'THE LIBERTY BELL'

The Liberty Bell is a very special bell - it is The Symbol of Freedom and Independence! For many years it was in Independence Hall - that is where I first saw it - many years ago. It now has a home of its own - Independence Plaza, across the street from Independence Hall.

The Continental Congress contracted with a foundry in France, to make The Liberty Bell. It came forth from the foundry, with a terrible flaw - the whole side of the bell was cracked open. The Continental Congress refused the flawed bell. The next bell came forth the same. After several failures, The Continental Congress decided to accept the bell with its awful crack or flaw.

The Liberty Bell - with its flaw - has become a symbol of a great Nation, whose goal is "Freedom and Justice for all" - that has not yet reached that goal. Our system of government - 'of the People, by the People, for the People' - the best on earth - yet, needs perfecting!

May God grant us Vision, Wisdom, Strength, and great Love and Devotion and Perseverance to work at perfecting it. Thus, may it ever 'Ring Loud and Clear for the last and the least - for ALL'

'A GREAT SERENDIPITY OF LIFE!'

Baseball, peanuts, popcorn, crackerjacks, coca cola, hotdogs, and apple pie - boy - that's ALL AMERICAN!

Hal Newhauser of The Detroit Tigers 1945 Championship Team was interviewed by Bryant Gumbel on The Today Show, October 9, 1984. They were talking about the 1984 World Series about to be underway, and reflecting back almost 40 years ago to the games between The Detroit Tigers and The New York Giants in The 1945 World Series. They showed a clip of Tiger Stadium of Detroit, and one of those Series games. And, they focused on the very section of the stadium, where I was sitting, to see a Doubleheader of The 1945 World Series, I was there, thanks to the kindness and loving generosity of my beloved Aunt Ethel and Uncle Jack Ross of Detroit, Michigan. (Mr and Mrs. John Franklin Ross, whose name I bear.)

A country boy, from Caddo, Alabama, from the pasture-baseball field league, led by Quinton Lentz. I was visiting an Aunt and Uncle, and would have the wonderful privilege of sharing the 1945 World Series - Glory of Baseball!

The short visit by way of The Today Show was this day, a Serendipity - indeed - an unexpected fond remembrance and reliving of a treasured moment in time!

'A 25 CENT FEAST - OUTING - AND CURE FOR THE FISHING FEVER'!

As a student pastor of three small, rural churches, I received only some $25.00 a week salary, And, that won't buy much meat for a wife and son, even in 1952. In fact, it won't pay the car payment, utilities, and gas to go to college, some 35 or 40 miles each way, and leave much for anything else. Certainly, it didn't leave much for entertainment or such. And, I love to go fishing - in fact, I often had 'fishing fever' - bad!

Lauren Elizabeth Phillips is holding a platter of 'crappie fillet' for a 'Family Feast'!

The only known remedy for fishing fever - or so I had heard from the old sages all my life - was to go fishing, One day as my classes ended, I had 'fishing fever' - bad, I checked my pockets and found I had one quarter - 25 cents - to my name. With that quarter, I could buy a half dozen minnows - that's all. When I asked the store attendant for a quarter's worth of minnows, he thought that I was kidding - but, I was dead serious, and 'antsy' to get to fishing!

When, I got to the rock pile, a favorite fishing place, a couple of hours before sun down, there were 2 old men fishing at my favorite fishing hole. I asked them if the fish were biting, and they reported, "Not much, we have been here about all day, and have only a couple of crappie each." About that time, they were loosing the last of a bucket full of minnows, and I was catching my 1st, crappie. I didn't lose the minnow, that I caught the first crappie with, and moments later, I was catching my second and third ones with it too!

This stirred up the old men, and they asked me to sell them a dozen minnows. I told them that I couldn't, that I just had a few - not wanting to tell them what I had done. They wouldn't give up, so, I gave them one each, which they almost immediately lost, and no fish.

In a little while, we all three left, and I had turned the 25 cents worth of minnows (only 4 that I had used) into six, beautiful, fat, black speckled crappie, for a fine, bountiful, and delicious platterful of fish for my family. With that platter of crappie, we also had hushpuppies made from The Mart Barber Grist Mill of Belgreen, where I was the Methodist Pastor. Mr. Mart always supplied his Preacher with corn meal for his family's table! Thanks, be unto The Lord our God! And, I am sure that we had potatoes and cabbage from my garden to add to the bounty!

Again and again, I was affirmed in so many ways, how truly - "God Cares for His Own!" *Peter 5:7*

'MY EARTHWORM FRIENDS!'

I am scattering earthworms in my garden to help build it up to its best. Photo by my dear Friend and next door neighbor, Rev. Ernest Dover.

My co-laborers in the development of my garden - as American Indian People would say - my Brothers! We have worked together to change that sticky old clay into a rich, humus, loamy soil, that is so great for gardening!

I saved the lives of hundreds, maybe even thousands, from death - from being crushed by the roaring, mighty wheels of our street (that is from their perspective) - so that they might live and work with me, in the fulfillment of a great purpose. That Purpose is: 'Learn to Live in Harmony with Mother Earth' - take good care of her and she will take good care of you!

And, as my dear wife, sweetheart, and friend and I, have 'Broken Bread together at our table' - I have often remarked, "My dear, we have 7 things from the garden, in our dinner today! Marvelously fresh, and delightfully nutritious - corn on the cob, Kentucky Wanders, squash, beets, lettuce, tomatoes, peppers, and onions, etc. - and, of course, cornbread - what a feast!

Thanks, be unto God! And, as my Cherokee People might say, Brother earthworm, thank you too!

'SUPER GRAINS CEREAL OF MY 'DAILY BREAD'

There are many values in the daily bowl of cereal and fruit that I eat, as part of my, 'Daily Bread' (meaning all the foods or nourishment that I take in.).

1st, there is great nutritional values in eating multi-grains. My bowl of cereal includes oats, brown rice, corn, and two ancient Super-Grains - Kumut, a wheat of the ancient Egyptian people, and Amaranth, the ancient sacred grain of the Aztec Indians of Central America, and the 3rd, is Oat Bran.

Amaranth contains the most perfect amino acid known on earth, according to a letter that I received from Dr. Robert Rodale. This amino acid is vital to enable the human body to make the best possible use of

Part of my 'Daily Bread', multigrains, some 8 grains, including Amaranth - The Aztec Indian Super Grain Gift to the Human Family! A daily bowl of these great whole grains, and fruits are nourishing, enabling the body to make fullest use of other nutrients it takes in, and provides me with vital regularity. Thanks be unto God! (Health Valley-The History of Amaranth, and Organic Golden Flax Cereal.)

all nutrition it takes in. (1)

These three grains that I mix in my breakfast bowl - Kamut, Amaranth, and Quaker Oat Bran, or Fiber One, are, for me at least, a God-send for helping my body with its essential regularity.

These three grains are rich in fiber and bran, that will help clean the inner walls of intestines, and thereby greatly reduce the possibility of colon cancer.

I have found that in eating this cereal and a cup of chopped fruit (fresh or frozen), and a slice of bread and jelly (in my case, sugar free), I feel better than when I ate an old traditional breakfast of homemade biscuits, jelly, butter, eggs, bacon, or sausage, or country ham, and 'redeye' gravy! And, I go most every morning until lunch time, without feeling hungry or weak in the middle of my stomach.

Of course, there is the added value of the fruit. Altogether, it is an approach to breakfast and nutrition that many millions, even billions, could live with!

'BEHOLD THE POTTER AT THE WHEEL'

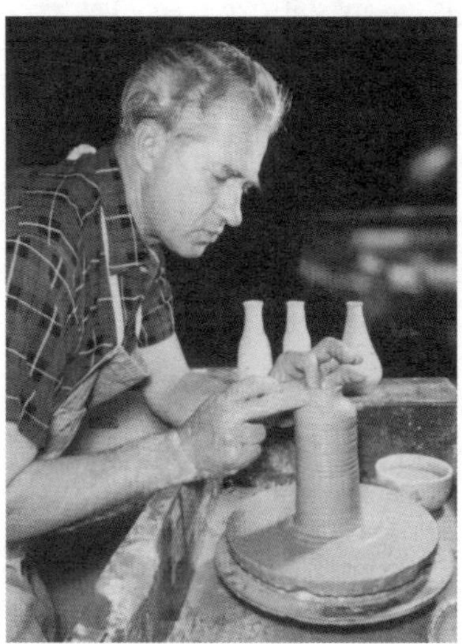

Douglas Ferguson

There is great and universal fascination with the potter's wheel, or the potter at work at the wheel, shaping the clay into a thing of beauty! This is surely, one of the most romanticized arts or professions on earth. It is indeed one of the oldest, going back thousands of years, into ancient Israel, and The Fertile Crescent. Many persons, in every age, going back for many thousands of years, have been quite caught up with the work and art of the potter.

The American Indian began the development of pottery several thousand years ago. The earliest pottery on this continent has been found in the shell mounds on Sapelo Island. Georgia. These date some 4,000 years ago. The American Indian developed many pleasing designs and created many beautiful items of pottery. But, they did not develop the wheel. (1)

There is something intrinsically beautiful about taking a lump of wet clay, throwing it on the potter's wheel, and with gifted, skilled, and patient touch, bringing forth a needed or desired object, or work of art! Now, listen to Jeremiah, in the parable of the potter, 18:1-12, as he watches the potter at his work. He sees the dissatisfaction of the potter, (The Creator), in some imperfection, and reshapes it, into something beautiful and good! (2)

I remember, with special fondness, our family in 1969, as part of a trip through Colorado, The Rocky Mountains, The Bad Lands, and Mount Rushmore, visited The Van Briggle Pottery and Museum in Colorado Springs. How truly inspiring to watch the potter at work, creating, bringing forth such beauty and art! (3)

And, what a word they have on their Van Briggle Pottery brochure - 'The skies of Colorado, ablaze with the colors of sunset and clothed in the Mysteries of earth's darker palette, have perpetuated in Colorado's clay......Come..........'See the oldest art........ throwing on the Potter's wheel, at Van Briggle Art Pottery!'

1. *Vase from the wheel of The Van Briggle Art Pottery, and a lump of fresh potter's clay, to use in The Children's Moment at First United Methodist Church, Fayette, Alabama.*
2. *A potter at work.*
3. *Brochure from Van Briggle Pottery.*

To return to china ware for a moment — there are three kinds of porcelain — hard paste, soft paste and a so-called artificial porcelain generally known as bone china. It gets its name because it contains a quantity of bone ash. It holds a middle place between hard and soft paste.

The history of pottery ware is so long that it takes many pages to tell only its high points. Encyclopedias and reference books on pottery art will give you much information if you are interested in learning more about history's oldest art.

Museums all over the world show pottery displays. Our own Pioneers Museum next to our public library displays a number of choice old pieces.

The first artist was not the cave man who drew pictures on the walls of his abode. The primitive maker of crude clay platters and bowls was history's first artisan. It was he who found out how to mix different clays, how to add minerals to make different colors. Each step was a forward one and marked the passing of ages all thru his patient experiment and effort.

Tour your own home! Look at the bases of the pottery you will find there. You will find most of them marked. Turn your dishes over and see if the maker put his mark on them. You may be surprised at the number of countries that are represented in your home.

Most studios have a hallmark as well as a name. One of the oldest and best known in this country is the Van Briggle mark which is a double "A" in a square

and this mark is on the bottom of every piece of Van Briggle ware made for the past 68 years in Colorado Springs, Colorado.

THROWING ON THE POTTER'S WHEEL

THE OLDEST ART IN HISTORY

Compliments of the VAN BRIGGLE ART POTTERY Colorado Springs, Colorado

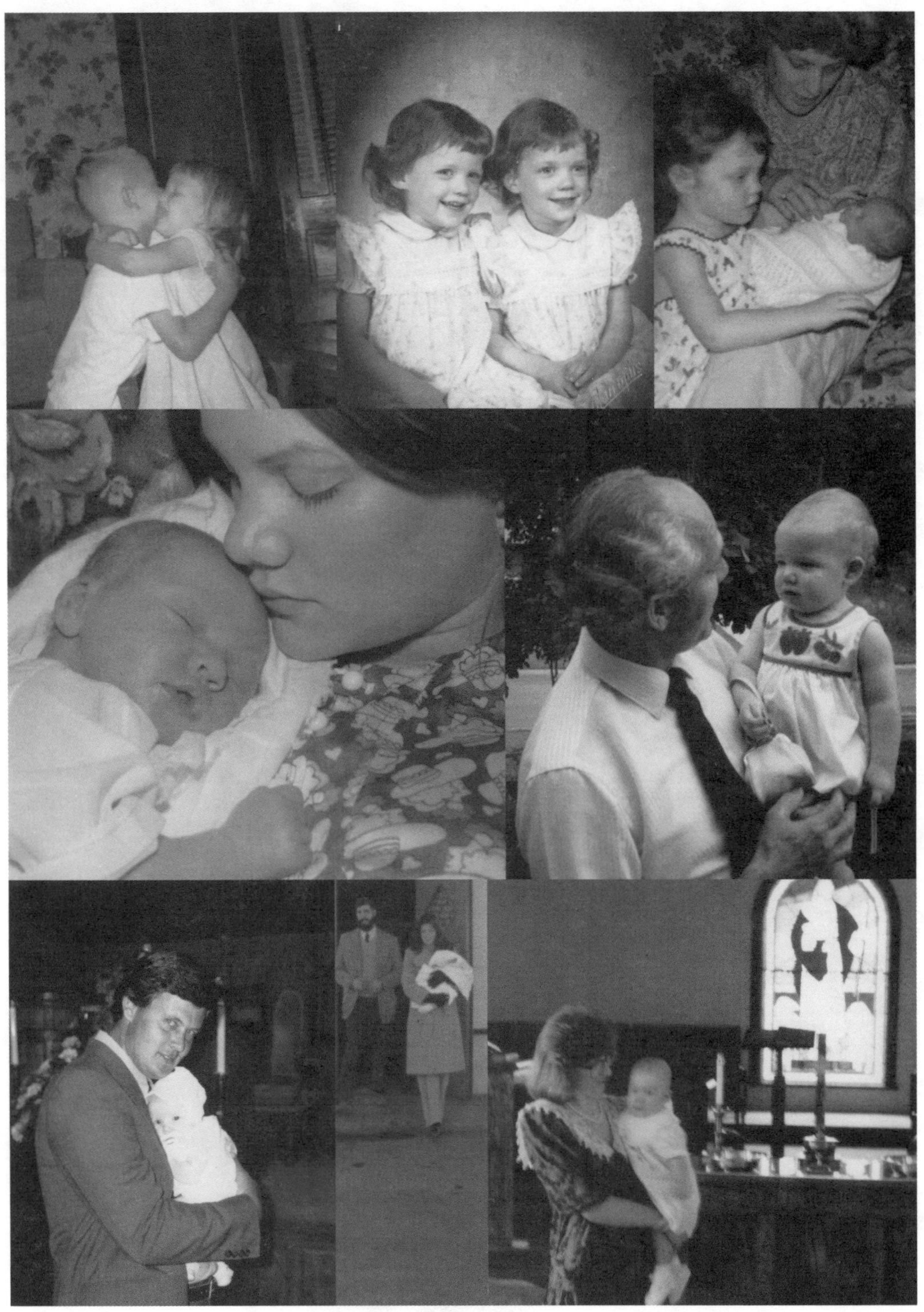

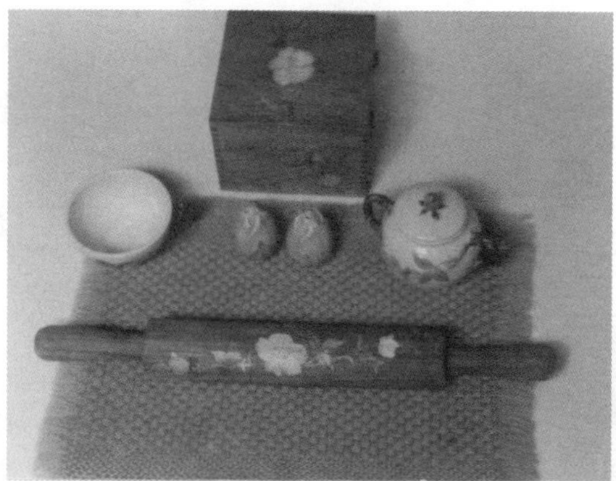

Cedar rolling pin given to my wife , Frances., by a dear friend. Diane Thompson painted the motif of our dishes on the rolling pin and recipes box.

'LOVE IS A TWO-WAY STREET'

Many of our lives have been touched and blessed by persons that we call, 'special persons'- mentally challenged individuals.

A good many years ago, my wife, Frances, and I developed a friendship with a mentally challenged person, who attended our church. On numerous occasions, we drove him home after church. We never expected more than his regular, gracious, "Thank you so much."

One Sunday, after driving him home, he presented my wife with a gift. He had found a chunk of cedar, and with his pocket knife had whittled out a somewhat crude rolling pin.

I took it, and had another friend to paint the motif of my wife's dishes (Desert Rose) on it. Today, it is a cherished treasure in our home. Above all, it is a reminder of a treasured friendship of yesteryear, and a reminder that 'Love is indeed a two-way street!'

'DEAL WITH YOUR FEARS!'

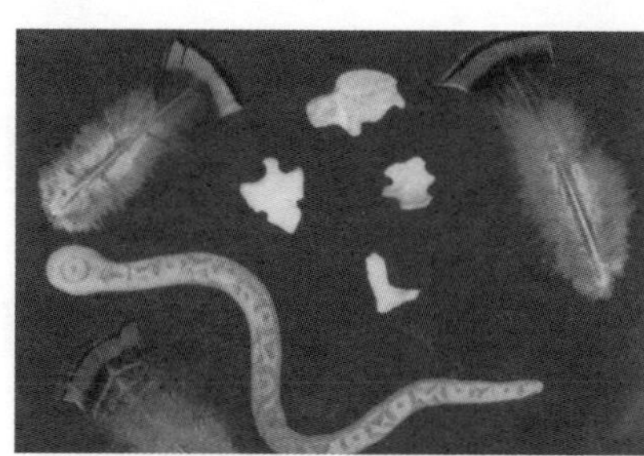

Effigies of The American Indian-Buffalo, Eagle, turtle, man's foot and leg, snake.

The failure or refusal to deal with and control our fears can get us into a heap of trouble. It is natural to have fears. It is just the better part of wisdom to learn to face them and deal with them.

Sudden and strange noises can frighten us, and is very hard to control. Some fears, though, like the fear of dogs, snakes, etc. are usually instilled in us by our parents, and/or other adults in our lives, while we are small children, to help safeguard us.

Three of my lady parishioners were fishing one day. They were in an old, wooden boat, out in a five acre lake. They were all very much afraid of snakes. One of them always carried a shotgun along, when out fishing. This day, while fishing, out in the middle of the lake, one of them saw a snake under the front seat of the boat. She screamed, and they all panicked. They jumped up on the seats of the boat, and the one with the shotgun was about to shoot the snake - apparently, without considering that to do so would blow a very large hole in the bottom of the wooden boat. Neither of them had on their life jacket, not one of them could swim - when, Thank the dear Lord, the black caretaker saw the calamity, came running to the lakeside, yelling, "No, no, Miss Excelle, no no, Miss Excelle, don't do that!"

And Thank The Lord, she didn't shoot that snake. The caretaker - took care! - and got them all safely out on dry land! And, he killed the harmless - oh, I don't know so much about that - harmless snake! For that supposedly, harmless snake had almost cost three dear ladies their lives, and me three members of my church!

Unfounded, uncontrolled fear can get you into a heap of trouble!

'SAINT - ONE THROUGH WHOM THE LIGHT SHINES!'

Stained glass window at Fayette United Methodist Church.

Dr. William Barclay says that The Apostle Paul used this word, Polupoikilos, to describe The Grace of God. It meant the many-coloured Wisdom or Grace of God-the great, varied, marvelous, magnificent wealth of His Glory and Grace! The many splendored Grace of God This word, or this idea of Paul, may have been the inspiration that brought forth stained glass windows for use in the sanctuaries of the church. Millions of lives have been blessed and inspired by this development in the life of the Church.

Dr. Harry Haines tells the story of a little boy looking in wonder and amazement at the stained glass windows of a great and beautiful cathedral. He asked his mother, "Who are they?" She told him that they were saints. He replied, "I see, saints are someone who lets the light shine through." A good answer!

A saint is, indeed, someone who lets the Light and Love of God shine through their lives! Many persons who live in Birmingham, in thinking of such persons, might think of 'Brother Bryan'- truly, he was one who let The Light and Love of God shine through his daily life!

'I LOVE CELEBRATIONS OF LIFE!'

I watched a Celebration of the debut of little bluebirds into the world of trees and flying birds and bees. I saw one of our 2, not fully grown and feathered bluebirds, the ones that had been hatched in my green, bluebird house. That little bluebird, way up there on that limb in the big pine tree at the edge of my yard - how did it get there?

Something seemed very special about this occasion. 1st, I wondered how on earth that little bluebird, that only yesterday could scarcely fly a few feet, could have gotten way up there. Then, I noticed something very interesting, there were several grown or adult bluebirds around. Hey - there was a Celebration going on!

I wondered, if those other adult bluebirds were - just maybe the Grandparents? They would surely come to The Celebration! Surely, it would be a Family Affair!

Could it be that it was the neighbor bluebirds come to see the pretty little ones - with tongue in cheek.

The next few days, I heard Will Curtis on National Public Radio on "The Nature of Things". He said that bluebirds older brothers and sisters help take care of the late summer hatch, which these were. Hmm, now, that must have been the answer. The older brothers and sisters had come to Celebrate that their job was now completed - wheeee! And, Whoopee!

'THE SERENDIPITY, THE BIG ONE THAT DID NOT GET AWAY!'

The moment he started peeling the line off - I felt the challenge - patience - patience - don't let him get away!

I was drop fishing about bushes, brush, and tree tops for crappie. I was using a chartreuse colored crappie jig - a tiny one - with a live minnow, with the cork at about 3 or 4 feet deep. I dropped the bait at the end of a tree top, and the fish took it, and headed out into deep, open water.

I felt such a strong pull, that if I attempted to turn him, I felt sure, he would immediately break the small line, 6 pound test line, and the light equipment would not handle him. I felt the only hope of landing him - of ever seeing what I had - wow - would be to let him work himself down. The only way that I could possibly land it would be to wear it out. The fish peeled out some 50 to 75 yards of my new Zebco 33, and I feared there was little more line left.

I asked my son to paddle the boat away from the bushes, and allow the fish to work against the weight and pull of the boat also. He did , and some 20 or 30 minutes later, he basically paddled the boat toward the area the fish was in, and dipped it up. The fish was all played or worked out, and gave very little more fight.

It was a 14 pound, 30 inch, hybrid stripe from Smith Lake! It was the big one that did not get away!

'LOOKS CAN BE DECEIVING!'

I love the emphasis of Sheriff Andy Griffith about looks and Gifts. The Mayor could not imagine Ray representing his city in the great gathering, but Andy thought in terms of his great Gift of tone and singing.

No doubt, the Mayor was mortified when he saw Ray come on the stage in his backwoodsy look. But, he swelled with pride when the crowd was caught up with the beautiful presentation of music.

I remember the teacher's description of my dear friend, when 1st, she saw him walk on the stage to speak. She said, that when he came off the plane, his clothes looked like he had slept in them for days, and his hair was unbelievably rumpled and unkempt. She was the area's fine arts promoter, and took great pride in the culture of the area. She felt the people of culture and pride would be horrified by the sight of her chosen speaker, and turn him off!

She had chosen him, because she had been much impressed with the reports of his presentations in many, many place, and how well the crowds had responded to him. But, she had not expected this, and she was not prepared for this problem of his appearance.

She said that within minutes, he had the crowd in his hand. They were sitting on the edge of their seats, eagerly hearing and savoring every word. Now, she understood why he was a sought after speaker, all over the earth, and why he had spoken all over the earth, in fact, on every continent of the earth!

I saw Harry Denman pour oil on the troubled waters many times. What a man - what a Gift - what a persuasive voice for us to 'Love one another, even as He has Loved us!

'SUMATANGA'

The first time I was invited to work at Camp Sumatanga, as a counselor or family group leader, I was excited - about rest and fishing. You see, I had heard a person talking about the meaning of the name - Sumatanga-and thought they said it was a place of rest and fishing. Boy, oh boy - that was my kind of place! That was right down my line, for with my parish responsibilities and college work - I felt the need for rest. But, far more, I was greatly excited about the possibility of fishing, lots of fishing, for I had a passion for fishing. I still love to fish and hope I always will! But, I have learned to discipline it a bit better.

I learned that week at Camp how wrong my expectations were-there was no rest, and worse, there was no time for fishing! But, it was a great, and exciting and fulfilling experience. And, across the years since - more than a quarter of a century - going to Sumatanga, working and sharing with the youth camps at Sumatanga has been one of the greatest joys of my life!

The Vespers speaker referred to had actually said Sumatanga means a 'Place of Rest and Vision' - and indeed it does! It surely has for me!

The picture of the fireplace is done by Danny Roundtree, great friend of Sumatanga. He has focused on the large piece of wood salvaged from the burning of the lodge, with "This is the Day which the Lord has made" carved into it. Reverend David Hutto chose that piece of wood because he saw a Symbol of The Rising Sun on it, and felt there was the inspiration for and The Promise of 'A New Day!'

A view of the snow-covered north garden of the United Nations Headquarters showing the statue entitled "Let us Beat Swords Into Ploughshares" by the Soviet sculptor Evgeny Vuchetich. The Statue, a gift from the Soviet Union presented in December 1959, is a bronze figure of a man holding a hammer in one hand and, in the other, a sword which he is making into a ploughshare. It symbolizes man's desire to put an end to war and convert the means of destruction into creative tools for the benefit of all mankind. - UN/DPI Photo by Evan Schneider, Copyright United Nation

Plaza of The United Nations - courtesy of The United Nations.

'BEAT YOUR SWORDS INTO PLOWSHARES! SHELLS INTO BELLS OF JOY!'

The great picture backdrop for the 1984 Missions Conference at Lake Junaluska, was of a man beating a sword into a plowshare. How fitting this great Biblical image and challenge, in a day when the threat of nuclear war hangs like a pall over our world.

An inspiring response to this challenge, comes from the war-torn land of Kampuchea (Cambodia). Missionaries, Margaret and Dean Hancock, tell the following story: "Near On Dong, the countryside is still littered with spent shell casings, remnants of the intense fighting in that area. Today, children scour the fields, gather the empty casings, and take them to village foundries. There, women and older persons melt the casings and remold them into bells. The bells are then placed on the harness of the oxen, animals indispensable to agriculture and transportation in Kampuchea." Shells into Bells - a witness to the transformation God makes possible in every human situation. They sent me one of those Bells!

And the children who share my 'Children's ministry', in The Hamilton United Methodist Church, have had a small part in their endeavor of Peace, through a Love Offering! May the Bells ever ring out a great melody of joy and Peace and Love!

Watching the ducks at Lake Junaluska.

' I LEARNED FROM THE DUCKS!'

Many persons were fascinated by the ducks at lake Junaluska, and, one of those was me! There were so many ducks - papa ducks - mama ducks - teenager ducks-and children ducks, I mean little ducklings.

The ducks had learned to come near to the people at times and they could expect to be fed - in fact, I think their chattering and quaking showed that they expected to be fed!

I learned that the little ones must go to school. Mama duck taught them. When the little ducklings got too close to suit mama duck, she harshly or sternly ordered them to come near to her, and, I never saw one not obey! It seemed that they had learned well, the importance of listening to, and obeying mama duck!

Helen Keller's birthplace in Tuscumbia, Alabama.

'HELEN KELLER - FIRST LADY OF COURAGE!'

Helen Adams Keller was born in Tuscumbia, Alabama on June 27, 1880. Her home place is called, "Ivy Green". She was born physically whole, but at eighteen months of age, Helen was stricken by a fever, that was diagnosed by the doctor as brain fever. There are those that feel the evidence indicates it may have been scarlet fever. The tragedy was the illness left Helen blind, deaf, and mute. It left her wild, unruly and with little understanding of the world around her.

When she was about six years old, her parents carried her to Baltimore to see Dr. Chrisholm, an eminent oculist. He offered no hope of improving her eyes, but told her parents that Dr. Alexander Graham Bell could help them with education possibilities for Helen. Helen says of that interview with Dr. Bell, that "would be the door through which I would pass from darkness into light, from isolation to friendship, companionship, knowledge, love."

Dr. Bell advised Mr. Keller to contact the Perkins Institution in Boston about securing a teacher. This he did at once, and Perkins sent a teacher, Miss Anne in March of 1887, to Tuscumbia to work with Helen. Helen says of this, "Thus I came up out of Egypt (symbolic of bondage), and stood before Sinai (symbolic of her experience of Grace and miracles), and a power divine touched my spirit and gave it sight, so that I beheld many wonders. And from the sacred mountain I heard a voice which said, "Knowledge is love and light and vision."

A new day began to dawn for Helen, when Miss Sullivan began working with her. When Helen was almost seven year of age, one of the great miracles in human drama began to unfold. This near savage child was changed into a responsive human being, and her marvelous mind and courageous spirit were awakened. The miracle began to blossom forth like a beautiful rose, at the outdoor water pump, where Miss Sullivan was pumping water over Helen's hand, and spelling out w-a-t-e-r. Helen says of this experience, "Somehow the mystery of language was revealed to me. I knew then, that 'w-a-t-e-r' meant the wonderful, cool, something flowing over my hand. That living word awakened my soul, gave it light, hope, joy, set it free! There were barriers still, it is true, but barriers that could in time be swept away - as we returned to the house every object which I touched seemed to quiver with life. When Helen realized the meaning and understood it was water flowing over her hand, she touched the earth and wanted it's name, and by nightfall she knew thirty words!

Helen entered Ratcliffe College in 1900, and received her bachelor of arts degree - Cum Laude-in 1904. She was the first deaf, blind person ever to graduate from college. In 1902, while in Ratcliffe, she wrote, THE STORY OF MY LIFE. Which is today published in fifty languages of the earth.

From 1906, until her death in 1968, Helen worked untiringly on behalf of blind and deaf-blind persons. In 1924, she joined the American Foundation for the Blind, and after World War 11 she traveled all over the world to promote the establishment of programs for the blind, in developing countries, for the American Foundation for Overseas Blind (now Helen Keller International). In later years, she became interested in bettering conditions for the blind in underdeveloped and war-ravaged countries. She lectured in more than twenty five countries and the five major continents. Wherever she appeared, she brought new courage to millions of blind people.

Well scene at Ivy Green where 'The Miracle' happened in the life of Helen Keller.

Bishop Philip Brooks was a dear friend of Helen. On one occasion, she asked him about her concern of so many religions in the world. To which he replied, "There is one universal religion, Helen, the religion of love. Love your Heavenly Father with your whole heart and soul, love every child of God as much as ever you can, and remember that the possibilities of good are greater than the possibilities of evil, and you have the key to heaven."

The Miracle Helen experienced at the pump enabled her, as it were, to come alive and catch the vibrations of life. And truly she came alive. And even more beautifully, she came alive to reach out and touch other such handicapped lives and help and encourage them to realize their God given potential. Surely, Helen Keller, First Lady of Courage, will forever show forth to the world that there are no boundaries to courage and faith - no boundaries to the Courageous Human Spirit set Free!

'A SERENDIPITY-HOPING, SKIPPING ROPE, CATCHING FROGS, AND OTHER WONDERFUL SURPRISES!'

A serendipity is an unexpected experience or revelation along the way. Such happened for me under the great old Magnolia tree in front of The School for The Deaf at Talladega, Alabama.

Dr. King Vivian, whom I had first met during the '1948 Conference Year', at District Conference at Henagar, Alabama, was our Pastor's School Preacher, in the summer of 1949. During one of the Worship Services, Dr. Vivian had told about various places that he had served as a Methodist Preacher. His story made me feel that he might have known my Maternal Grandmother's brother, the Reverend Dr. Charley Tildon Talley, who had died some 10 years before, while Pastor of The University Church, near Texas A & M University. Family being so very important to me then - and it still is - I timidly asked Dr. Vivian if he had known Dr. Talley.

I will never forget that moment! This great, and widely known Preacher, and much sought after speaker, of The Methodist Church, invited me to go sit with him under that beautiful Magnolia tree, and talk awhile. He told me that Dr. Talley had been his Spiritual Mentor - his Spiritual Father. He had been his District Superintendent in Texas, and his mentor across the years, and that he had been the greatest influence and inspiration in his life!

I could hardly wait to get home - to tell Mother about the Wonderful, Exciting, Serendipity that God had given me that day!

You see, I remembered being so excited one day in 1939, when I went to the mail box, and got a post card from Uncle Charley, from Bryan, Texas, he had written that he was coming by Courtland, Alabama, to visit our family, enroute to The Conference of Union. I was so excited with the anticipation of his visit - but, he didn't come - instead, we received word that he had died of a heart attack.

SECTION THREE:
SHARING A WORD OF FAITH AND HOPE!

With Wings of Eagles
Wait in the Spirit for Vision.
Seek for Wisdom,
Find the Strength to rise up.
and climb mountains,
to walk long trails,
And to soar
to Life's Heights!

Calligraphy - With Wings of Eagles - by Margurite Busby.

'THE EAGLE'

The eagle - beautiful, powerful, bird of prey - for many eons has been a source of great symbolic meaning and inspiration for much of mankind. Surely, the word from Isaiah 40:31, "They who wait on the Lord shall renew their strength, they shall mount up with wings like eagles, they shall run and not be weary, they shall walk and not faint", is one of the great words of inspiration!

I checked with Webster for data about the eagle and found, "The eagle was a military standard of ancient Rome. This symbol was adopted by France under Napoleon. The Bald Eagle is the white-headed earn or sea-eagle of America. This is the eagle which is emblazoned as the national emblem on the coat of arms of The United States, and is also represented on the coinage." (2)

The Eagle Dance of The Drama - 'Unto These Hills', at Cherokee, North Carolina.

I also checked Smith's Bible Dictionary, and he said the golden eagle lives in Israel, they live (as do the bald eagle) in pairs only; and require a wide range of country, five pairs occupying as much as twenty miles. (3)

The eagle was a great symbol in the ancient Hebrew faith. The Psalmist in 103:5 says, "So that your youth is renewed like the eagle's." The Hebrews were much impressed with the great strength of the eagle's wings and eyes. The great care of the eagle for its young became symbolic of our heavenly Father's care - "He found him in a desert land, and in the howling waste of the wilderness; he encircled him, he cared for him, he kept him as the apple of his eye. Like an eagle that stirs up its nest, that flutters over its young, spreading out its wings, catching them, bearing them on its pinions, the Lord alone did lead him, and there was no foreign god with him." (Deuteronomy 32:10-12)

Some Biblical scholars believe that in the ancient Hebrew's use of the eagle, there is an allusion to the phoenix legend. "In Egyptian mythology the phoenix is a fabulous bird which was said to exist single, be consumed by fire, and to rise again from

Stain glass window with Eagle Medallion

its own ashes with renewed youth and beauty; hence, an emblem of immortality." In Sources of Strength, President Jimmy Carter writes that, "He satisfies my desires with good things, so that my youth is renewed like the eagle's.... ." (5), (6)

The American Indian also derived much inspiration and strength from the eagle. One American Indian legend says that the eagle is able to fly high into the heavens and look The Great Spirit in the eye. (Here James Adair would undoubtedly argue that the Indian derives from the ancient Hebrew as evidenced by this similar concept.) And, another legend says the eagle bears up our prayers to The Great Spirit. (7)

The Eagle has influenced many Indian ceremonies, such as The Eagle Dance. Surely, those who have attended The Cherokee Drama, "Unto These Hills", in Cherokee, North Carolina, will never forget how beautiful, intense, and moving experience The Eagle Dance truly is! To witness such is to realize how The American Indian drew many symbolic meanings from the eagle to inspire and strengthen his own life.

Jon Magnuson, in an article, "Views from a Sacred Mountain", appearing in The Christian Century, August 1-8, 1984, tells about a group going to Mato Paba - Bear Mountain (Sacred Mountain of the Sioux and Cheyenne) to hold a Pipe Ceremony. Elmer Running, a shaman or medicine man from The Rosebud Reservation, begins to sing his song to the four directions and the scene is one of solemnness and reverence. Heads are bowed and prayers are being raised. An eagle soars overhead and Jon says, "And the winged one, who for that brief moment graced our presence, is believed by Native people to be a sign of blessing one of the Eagle people, inhabitants of a region between heaven and earth. The Pipe is being passed now, and prayers are being lifted up for all the earth, for animals, and for all living things broken and in need of healing." (8)

Its highest and most sacred meaning is the symbolic use by the Navajo Shaman or Medicine Man. Healing and strength are derived from the sand painting of eagle feathers by the medicine man.

I feel certain that when Thomas Jefferson, John Adams, and Benjamin Franklin were debating a National Symbol, the influence of the American Indian's love of the eagle was one of the strong factors in the decision. Thomas Jefferson and Benjamin Franklin were great students of the American Indian and were deeply influenced by the strong character and faith of the Indian. I am sure, they were also influenced by the Iroquois use of the symbol of the Eagle holding six arrows, representing The Six Nations of The Iroquois Confederacy. Thus, The Symbol of The Union of The Thirteen Colonies would be The Eagle holding 13 arrows in its claws.

Symbol of Eagle on top of the steeple of The Episcopal Church in Tuscaloosa, Alabama.

Thus, on June 20, 1782, the decision was made that The Bald Eagle would henceforth be The National Symbol of The United States of America! Thus, the "Free Spirit, high soaring, courageous bird - The Bald Eagle - became the symbol of America's strength, courage, and pride! (9)

An old symbol of the early Christian tradition is of the eagle with a fish in its talons, symbolic of The holy Spirit carrying the redeemed souls up to heaven. A lectern with an Eagle Symbol may be related to that faith, which is also similar to the faith of The American Indian, that the eagle can bear our prayers and worship to God or The Great Spirit. But, of all the symbolic meanings related to the eagle, the greatest, most inspiring to me, is that beautiful, majestic, image of Isaiah's 40:31 - "They that wait upon The Lord shall renew their strength; they shall mount up with wings as eagles; they shall run and not be weary; and they shall walk, and not faint!"

Credit is given The North Alabama Conference Bicentennial Committee for commissioning this painting by Danny Roundtree.

LEGEND OF BEAR-MEAT CABIN

Here we will endeavor to describe the development of the first Methodist Circuit in Alabama. Douglass, early in the Conference year of 1818, removed Ebeneezer Hearn from Flint Circuit, and sent him into the territory south of Madison County. The area had just been opened by the Treaty between General Andrew Jackson and The Creek Indians, after their surrender at Horseshoe Bend. The Treaty was signed August 9, 1814. Hearn was commissioned to survey this section, make preaching appointments, and where practical, to organize churches. Few men were better equipped to do this important work than Hearn, and he did his work well.

In April, 1818, Hearn set out for his work, crossed the Tennessee River at Ditto's Landing, and traveled through the lands of the Creeks. The first night was spent in the cabin of an Indian trader. At daybreak, he was again in the saddle, riding south. After a twenty-mile trip, he came to Bear-meat Cabin (the present-day Blountsville, for many years the seat of Blount County,). Here, he found a number of families, some of whom were Methodists. Here, he preached his first sermon, on his yet-to-be organized circuit, and arranged for another service, one month hence. This became one of the regular preaching places on his first circuit.

West says: "Hearn left Bear-meat Cabin, and came to 'Jones Valley', where Birmingham is today located, and found a large settlement, among them being Rev. David Owen, a Tennessean, who had moved there in 1817, and built a house less than half a mile from where stands Jefferson County Court House." Owen's home became Hearn's headquarters, and became the first house of Methodist worship in what is now the metropolitan city of Birmingham, more than half a century before there was any Birmingham. Owen's son, Thomas had settled in Jones' Valley in 1816, and was, with the Prude, Sadlers, McAdorys and others, prominent in planting Methodism in that area.

Hearn remained in that locality long enough to meet the Methodists who had moved in, then turned his horse's head in a southwesterly direction. His next stop was what is now Scottsville, Bibb County. After surveying this section, he moved some twenty miles to the Falls of Cahawba, now Centreville, the seat of Bibb County. That seems to have been the most southerly point visited on the first round. Whether or not he preached here on this first round is not known, though he probably did leave an appointment, to be filled on his second round.

He then traveled some twenty miles in a slightly northwesterly direction, and attended a love-feast at the residence of Obed (Obediah) Lovelady, near Wilson's Hill, now known as Montevallo." Wilson's Hill was settled by Jesse Wilson, one of Andrew Jackson's soldiers, and a kinsman of Mrs. Will F. Franke. Among the earliest settlers here were Obediah Lovelady and Edmund King. Later, four local preachers settled here, and were here to co-operate with Hearn. It was these four ordained Elders, J. D. Lee, Drewry Powell, Joseph Walker and Joshua West, who conducted the sacramental service in the Lovelady residence. Hearn himself had not yet been ordained deacon.

Anson West, no kin, so far as known, to Joshua West, quotes Hearn as saying, 'Here I organized the first Society I formed on my new mission, and here I had my first quarterly meeting." Some ten years later divergent views caused the organization of the Methodist Protestant Church, and Joseph Walker, "fiery and fanatical," to use West's description, "was one of the leading agitators," while Ebenezer Hearn, his son-in-law, and Robert L. Walker, his son, were among the chief defenders of the polity of the M. E. Church. West had no patience with "the turbulent party of innovators," and expressed himself in referring to them in language that was scarcely appreciated by them.

Joshua West, who co-operated in organizing the Church at Montevallo, gave more than 67 years to the local ministry. A large part of this time, he was a medical doctor and rendered a great service to hundreds of families in Shelby and Bibb counties. But, his first love was the Church, whose doctrines he knew, loved, and practiced. He assisted in establishing the camp-ground about five miles north of Montevallo, and named it "Ebeneezer", in honor of Hearn. Here, a society was organized, and Ebeneezer Church still prospers, as one of the churches on Camp Branch Circuit in The Sylacauga District. West died in 1860, and is buried beside his wife, (nee' Prentice), at Montevallo. He requested that there be inscribed upon his tombstone, the fact that he believed all the doctrines of The Methodist Church. The author has visited his grave, which has the following inscription: "Dr. Joshua West was born in Rockingham County, Virginia, 1771. Was licensed a Methodist preacher on the 17th, of October, 1792. Was ordained Deacon by Bishop Asbury, 7th, of October, 1792. Was licensed to practice medicine, 1812. Was ordained Elder by Bishop Asbury, 20th, of October,, 1813. He was a man of prayer and praise, having served his generation faithfully as a preacher for nearly 68 years. He died 8th, of January, 1860, believing in every one of the doctrines of The Methodist Church - age 91 years."

Hearn next traveled for about sixty miles to Catawla Town, now Ashville, the seat of St.Clair County. Here, he organized a society. Between Wilson's Hill and Catawla Town, he established a preaching place. He, then returned to Bear-meat Cabin, having "in some measure" formed a circuit.

It is not the kind of circuit that most today relate to, or think of. It is certainly not like the

1st, circuit that I was appointed to - Cotaco Circuit - in 1949. The 4 churches that I served while living at Cotaco (or Woodland Mills of Cotaco County as it was known in the days of Bear-meat Cabin.) were: Cotaco, Red Oak Grove, Antioch Methodist Churches, and Tallucha Presbyterian Church.

AMERICA

The Liberty Bell (National Treasure and symbolic parable) - with its awful flaw or crack - as it appeared in Independence Hall, Philadelphia, Pa.

America, there is something beautiful, hauntingly beautiful about that name! It brings forth in our minds many images - as the grain laden plains, the rolling rivers, the dashing and roaring mountain streams, the majestic mountains, the quiet villages with many steeples and the teeming, towering cities; or again those great concepts of 'The land of the free and the home of the brave', and "of the people, by the people, for the people" - which I believe is the greatest concept of government man has ever conceived.

America - from her very inception in the minds of great men like Thomas Jefferson and Benjamin Franklin, and through her birth under such able leadership as George Washington, she has been destined under the Mighty hand of God for greatness and for world leadership!

America - though infant in the eyes of the world, there was great strength - the strength of her people - at her very birth! As part of a great time of national rejoicing and celebration, the Liberty Bell was cast, to be the symbol of her great freedom and strength! But the Liberty Bell came forth cracked - a great flaw in it - and subsequent efforts to make her perfect failed, and at last the bell with its flaw was accepted! And today it stands enshrined in a park across the street from Independence Hall.

Through the years this symbol has spoken to us of the beauty and strength of this great Nation and her people! But, I believe the flaw in The Liberty Bell has reminded us, individually and as a nation, again and again that there are flaws in our system of government, or The American way of Life, that needs correcting and perfecting. Though this is the greatest nation or government on Earth, it is not without flaw, and our love for America should move us to work together to the end that it shall be perfected! This is the note, I believe that Katherine Lee Bates in the beautiful national hymn, America, underlines in the phrases, 'God mend thine every flaw' and 'may God thy gold refine'. And under God, may we all join in that dedication!

When the sectional issues of economics, erroneously seen and often projected as only the issue of slavery, set brother against brother and threatened to tear the country apart permanently, under such noble and able leadership as Abraham Lincoln, we were able to weather the storm. Even through this time of intense agony and great suffering, This Nation, under God, gained statute and strength!

Again, as our people rallied under the banner of 'Making the world safe for Democracy', with the able and dedicated leadership of Woodrow Wilson, our people and nation grew in statute and strength!

But we had not faced our most difficult and challenging test or trial. We met our most challenging and agonizing test in the issue that the world's most noble and notable political achievement: The American Declaration of Independence and The Constitution of The United States (in particular, The Bill of Rights) did not mean the same for each and for all! Thus in the great Civil Rights Struggle we had to bare our souls and deal with our national flaw in The Liberty Bell, I believe God has been calling us to agonize and struggle to that point where we can speak and deal with integrity, where as President Jimmy Carter says. "All can have both personal liberty and equality of opportunity!"

Many lives and voices have spoken to this issue, as we have struggled and struggle with it. Among those who have surely spoken to my heart and life in these matters are President John F. Kennedy and Rev. Wallace Hamilton. From the podium and the pen in such almost classic works as *The Thunder of Bare Feet*, Wallace Hamilton has challenged us, as loyal and committed Americans, to work at our flaws until at last through the Grace of God our Liberty Bell shall indeed ring forth loud, and clear, and true for one and all! Let Freedom Ring!

It is altogether fitting as we come to this time of National Celebration - our National Bicentennial Celebration - July 4, 1976, that we, individually and collectively, dedicate ourselves anew to this great challenge before us! And pray God the Dream - The Greatest Such Dream of All Time - 'Of the people, by the people, for the people' that has lived in and haunted so many minds and spirits across the years, may continue to burn deeply in our souls. May God hasten the day when, through persevering in this Dream, we shall stand at last, 'ONE PEOPLE'- 'ONE NATION UNDER GOD, INDIVISIBLE, WITH LIBERTY AND JUSTICE FOR ALL! And at last. all the joys, blessings, and benefits of this great Nation shall be for all her people! So Mote it be!

ABRAHAM LINCOLN

President Abraham Lincoln
courtesy of The National Archives.

A big man physically, a giant in strength of character. He is the tallest man to serve as President of The United States of America.

Abraham was born February 12, 1809, in a little log cabin (about fourteen feet square) on the 'Sinking Spring' farm, near Hodgenville, in Hardin County, Kentucky. Little Abe's bed was in the loft and was made of leaves and straw, with the skins of wild animals for coverings.

His mother, Nancy Hanks Lincoln was a strong and good influence on his life. When a log schoolhouse was opened in their community she laid her gaunt, toil-worn hand upon Abe's head and said, "You must learn the alphabet and master the spelling book. You must learn to read and write. You must get knowledge, so that when you grow up you will be wise and good." Abe would have the opportunity to go to school, crude as they were and with poorly trained and equipped teachers, for less than a year of formal education. But with the encouragement of his dear mother and a great love of books he read avidly the books he could borrow. By the light of fire in the fireplace, Abe read The Bible, Aesop's Fables, Robinson Crusoe, Bunyan's, Pilgrim's Progress, A History of The United States , The Life of Henry Clay, and Weem's, Life of Washington. In later life, Abraham Lincoln would look back upon his life and the influence of this period and say, "God bless my mother. All that I am or ever hope to be I owe to her." (2)

In preparation for his first job, out on his own as an adult, Abe split 1400 rails for a Mrs. Miller, to weave enough cloth and make him a pair of trousers. This earned him the lifelong nickname of the 'Rail Splitter'. (3)

When Abe was twenty two years old, he took a boat load of provisions and stock down the Mississippi River to the market in New Orleans. While there, he saw gangs of slaves chained and driven through the streets like cattle; he saw them cruelly whipped and sold in the slave market; he saw families separated and children heartlessly taken away from their parents. These sights depressed him greatly, and he said, “If I ever get a chance to hit slavery, I’ll hit it hard.” (4)

When, he returned home, young Abe took a job running a store, where he earned the title - ’Honest Abe’. During this time, he was also the postmaster and surveyor , and studied law. When Lincoln entered politics, he was a tall, gawky-looking fellow, wearing a wide-brimmed straw hat without a band, a homespun shirt, and a claw-hammer coat, and tow trousers that did not meet his shoes by several inches. The crowds first saw him as a clown, but when he spoke, they were so impressed they elected him. In 1834, he was elected to the Illinois Legislature for the first of four terms. His election appears to have been due to his great physical strength, his sense of humor, his tolerance, his reputation for honesty, and the purity of his life. In 1846, he was elected to Congress.

In 1858, while running as a candidate for The United States Senate, Lincoln made his famous statement about “A house divided cannot stand” - which revealed the influence of The Bible on his

Four score and seven years ago our fathers brought forth, upon this continent, a new nation, conceived in Liberty, and dedicated to the proposition that all men are created equal.

Now we are engaged in a great civil war, testing whether that nation, or any nation, so conceived, and so dedicated, can long endure. We are met here on a great battle-field of that war. We have come to dedicate a portion of it as a final resting place for those who here gave their lives that that nation might live. It is altogether fitting and proper that we should do this.

But in a larger sense we can not dedicate — we can not consecrate — we can not hallow this ground. The brave men, living and dead, who struggled here, have consecrated it far above our poor power to add or detract. The world will little note, nor long remember, what we say here, but can never forget what they did here. It is for us, the living, rather to be dedicated here to the unfinished work which they have, thus far, so nobly carried on. It is rather for us to be here dedicated to the great task remaining before us — that from these honored dead we take increased devotion to that cause for which they here gave the last full measure of devotion — that we here highly resolve that these dead shall not have died in vain; that this nation shall have a new birth of freedom, and that this government of the people, by the people, for the people, shall not perish from the earth.

The Gettysburg Address as hand written by President Lincoln.

"A house divided against itself cannot stand." I believe this government cannot endure permanently half slave and half free. I do not expect the Union to be dissolved—I do not expect the house to fall—but I do expect it will cease to be divided. It will become all one thing, or all the other. Either the opponents of slavery will arrest the further spread of it, and place it where the public mind shall rest in the belief that it is in the course of ultimate extinction; or its advocates will push it forward till it shall become alike lawful in all the States, old as well as new, North as well as South.

Lincoln Springfield Speech, Close of Republican State Convention, June 16, 1858.

With malice toward none; with charity for all; with firmness in the right, as God gives us to see the right, let us strive on to finish the work we are in; to bind up the nation's wounds; to care for him who shall have borne the battle, and for his widow, and his orphan—to do all which may achieve and cherish a just and lasting peace among ourselves, and with all nations.

Lincoln, Second Inaugural Address, March 4, 1865.

life. This statement did much to gain him such public attention and support as to enable him to be elected President of The United States in 1861. (5)

Lincoln Memorial

Lincoln declared The Declaration of Independence meant that all men are equal in their right to life, liberty, and the pursuit of happiness. He wanted principles that would stand the test of time, and square with eternal justice. January 1, 1863, Lincoln issued The Emancipation Proclamation - proclaiming all slaves free. This made Abraham Lincoln immortal. The great gentle heart and tolerance of Lincoln is seen in his immortal words, "With malice toward none and with charity for all." It was the dream and plan of this great man to bind up the nation's wounds and to establish firmly a reunited country - to save The Union!

In 1864, with the tide of the great and dark struggle - The Civil War - drawing to an end, Lincoln was elected to a second term as President. Shortly after, he would deliver another of his immortal addresses - The Gettysburg Address. In the celebrating of the end of the war, Lincoln and his wife went to Ford's Theater in Washington, D.C., on the evening of April 14, 1865. During the performance, an evidently deranged actor, John Wilkes Booth, shot President Lincoln, through the head. The next morning, as he died, Secretary of State, William Seward said, "Now, he belongs to the Ages." (6)

Lincoln was a participant in Church, but never a member, about which he said, "When any church will inscribe over its altar as its sole qualification for membership, 'Thou shalt love the Lord Thy God with all thy heart and with all thy soul and with all thy mind and thy neighbor as thyself' that church will I join with all my heart and with all my soul. (7)

His great and unchanging creed was - 'Righteousness exalteth a Nation'. Truly, he was a giant among men!

NATIVE AMERICAN AWARENESS -
THE RICHNESS OF AMERICA IN HER INDIAN HERITAGE!
Acts 10:17-23, & Romans 1: 8-14

Let me do something of a Report-today- on what God is doing through The United Methodist Church with Native Americans in The Southeast. Not for or to Native Americans, but, in a working-sharing relationship with Native American People - as with Brothers and Sisters.

For the past 10 years, I have been chair of The Conference Committee on Native American Ministry, and The North Alabama Conference Representative to SEJANAM (Southeastern Jurisdictional Agency for Native American Ministry), and chair of The SEJANAM Committee on Program and Research, and a member of The Design Team.

We are called by The General Conference of The United Methodist Church to Awareness - to Native American Awareness - but, what does The United Methodist Church mean by: Awareness? Mr. Webster uses the words knowing, understanding, conscious of, and informed, in relation to awareness. But, what did The General Conference mean in 1988, when they set a day, as a special time to stress 'Awareness of Native Americans?'

1st, I believe they were saying to all Americans, that we need to make a conscious effort to get to know Native Americans as a People. We have spent so very little time and effort in getting to know them in and through our study of history. And, in getting to know them as a segment of our population, as participants in the life of the Nation of America, and, most important of all, as neighbors and friends - fellow Americans and fellow Christians!

2ndly, I feel we need to become more aware of the noteworthy achievements of The Native Americans or The American Indians, and how these achievements have contributed to all our lives, and especially how they have contributed to the strength of this great Nation of The United States of America! Truly, as The Apostle Paul says, "We are debtors" - we owe a great debt of gratitude to our Native American People!

The American Indian learned to adapt, and to live quite successfully in every area of the continent. That is, they achieved a sense of self-reliance. This means they could meet the basic needs of their families by a close association with, and a dependency on Mother Earth. They learned to take from Mother Earth only what they needed in order to sustain their lives. Thus, they developed great survival skills. They learned what foods could be found in nature, how to hunt and fish productively, yet without undue waste, or taxing of Nature's resources. The 1st, White men found the American Indian very self-reliant, and great conservationists - caring for and loving Mother Earth!

One of the things Dr. Herscher pointed out to me, in a mini course on archeology, at The University of Georgia excavation of Burnt Indian Village, on the banks of The Chattahoochee River, in 1966, was how very little rubbish or throwaway was in the village dump. This trash dump or pit was in the midst of the village, and showed evidence of much of what they took as food, such as deer, turkey, beaver, fish, etc. For example, there was but little evidence of deer being used for food, though you can be sure they were, for the skins were used for clothing, moccasins, bedding, etc, and the bones were used for tools for digging and awls for punching holes in leather in sewing into garments or into moccasins, and sinews for bows and sewing, etc.

In his native state, The American Indian seemed to have had a natural inclination to exploring and testing for the use and value of many and various things. He seems to have tried most every thing that might be used for food, or as a source of medicine, probably got a lot of belly aches too! But, through such experimentation, they discovered, domesticated, and used many of the foods that we continue to use today - such as corn, beans, and squash. These 3 foods of the American Indian, through their generous, gracious, and neighborly attitude and spirit of sharing, became the most important foods of Colonial America! They, indeed, became the vital basis of our evolving economy!

I contend that DeSoto, in his exploration of The Southeast, looking for gold and other riches, found the finest farmers on earth - in part, along the Coosa Valley, among The Coosada or The Coushatta People. In a letter of request for answers to some questions of my research, The United States Department of Agriculture responded that some 60- 65% of the foods that we put on our tables today were domesticated by The American Indian People! (1)

In the same way, they found many sources of medicine that were usable and effective. There are those in modern medicine research today, who contend that, "We have not found a single medicinal value in nature in North America that some of the American Indian had not already found and used effectively". There are indications, that when the White Man first arrived on this continent, they found here the finest Medical Intern Program on earth. The National Geographic Magazine, October, 1991, reports that the American Indian was far ahead of Europe in Medicine in 1500. (2), (3)

The American Indian developed one of the world's great Faith approaches to life. 1st, Learn to Live in Harmony with The Great Spirit, The Giver of Breath. 2) Learn to Live in Harmony with Mother Earth. 3) Learn to Live in Harmony with all living things. 4) Learn to Live in Harmony with your fellow man! These great Spiritual Principles and Values of Life, influenced The American Indian to give those 1st, waves of explorers and colonists, a warm, friendly, and neighborly or helpful Welcome. Their Faith influenced the American Indian to give the newcomers, food, space for a village nearby, and help to get established. James Adair, who lived among the Indians for some 40 years and wrote a History of The American Indian, was very much convinced that the Faith of The American Indian was very much like that of The Ancient Hebrews of The Old Testament. (4), (5)

I am convinced that though The Greeks through their ancient Athens City-State experiment (which was mostly a slave state), The British through their Magna Carta, Mayflower Compact, and British Parliament, etc, contributed to the evolvement of The Democracy of The United States of America. Yet, I believe, The American Indian was the primary, the major source of the idea, the inspiration, and the encouragement for that great Experiment in Democracy in Philadelphia in 1776. The French and English writers of philosophy, such as Thomas More, John Locke, Montesquieu, Rousseau, Thomas Paine, Benjamin Franklin and Thomas Jefferson, etc., whose pamphlets saturated the colonies, and stirred the American and French Revolutions, drew much of their ideas, and inspiration from The American Indian - from his ideas, Councils, and his great love of freedom and democratic and egalitarian forms of government. And these writers, and The American Indian, especially The Iroquois, greatly influenced many of those who helped to frame our American Constitution, and formed our Union of Thirteen Colonies, especially Benjamin Franklin, Thomas Paine, Charles Thomson, and Thomas Jefferson. (6), (7)

Now, these Native Americans, who contributed so much to the development of this great Nation - America-were, for the most part, disenfranchised in and from their own homeland. Yet, as a People, they have been able to maintain a great and splendid spirit among them. The American Indian has, for the most part, kept Faith, and continued, and continues even to this good day, to have Hope for a better tomorrow. (Medallion-Symbol of Hope!)

And today, The United Methodist Church is endeavoring to respond to The Macedonian Cry of The Native American People for help - for greater awareness and appreciation of them, and for Ministries that are sensitive to their need and to their culture.

The General Conference , in 1980, called upon United Methodist Churches across The United States to become aware of Native American People - to receive with appreciation and Thanksgiving their gifts of their history, achievements, contributions, their very colorful and rich culture, and their spirituality. Speaking to this concern, The Smithsonian Museum has said, "We and our children can learn what Native Americans have to teach us about such things as 1)the delicate balance between people and nature..... 2) about their profound respect for family, 3) their ethic of sharing..... 4) about their deep spirituality, and 5) their magnificent art." (8)

In 1984, The Jurisdictional Conference at Lake Junaluska created SEJANAM, to respond to the new and growing concern for Native American People. I was soon asked to be a volunteer member of the team. SEJANAM set a goal of strengthening the existing 4 ministries of The Southeast, and to endeavor to establish new ministries wherever needed and wherever we could get an appropriate response.

We have endeavored to listen for and to Macedonian Cries of our Native American Brothers and Sisters. Sometimes, they were in the form of Dreams shared, as Mable Haught's Dream, for a Pastor and a Church for her Seminole People, and my dear Friend, the late Tom Queen, long time Director of The Cherokee Methodist Mission in Cherokee, North Carolina, for a Church in Greensboro, N. C. , for his People. Tom did not live to Celebrate its birth, but, Thanks be unto God, it is now a reality!

The new Native American Church in Greensboro received its first new members in January, 1994, 54 new members, with 20 baptisms! This new church received Urban Initiative Funding, and the pastor, Rev. Kenneth Locklear, a Lumbee Indian, received a Seminary Scholarship from Native American Awareness Offerings. In July, 1999, Kenneth is to become The Executive Director of SEJANAM, with office in Lake Junaluska.

Today, New Ministries are being considered for Atlanta, Knoxville, Nashville, Memphis, etc.-wherever there are large numbers of Native Americans. Ministry is a response to the felt and expressed needs of the people. To be sure, there are many needs and concerns yet to be heard, and many, many needs yet to be met. But, due to the response of The Church to hear The Macedonian Cry of our Native American Brothers and Sisters, there is a growing sign of Hope! A Sign that Native Americans are being accepted, appreciated, and encouraged to take part in the life and fellowship and Ministry of The Church. In our 1994 Jurisdictional Conferences, Seneca leaders ran for Bishop of The United Methodist Church.

The Native American International Caucus reports that, "Due to the response of The United Methodist Church, Native Americans are more visible in The Church today, than ever before; more intentional ministries have been developed; more appropriate ministries have been developed that are sensitive to the indigenous culture of The Native American." I believe a New and Brighter Day of Hope is Dawning!

May God grant us even more response in local churches, 1) seeking greater Awareness and 2) concern for the betterment of the People, and 3) pledging Advance Special support to SEJANAM, and that more and more Fruit may be borne to the building up of The Church, and to The Glory of God! Amen and Amen

"JESUS IS THE BREAD OF LIFE"

Few things stir up our taste buds like the aroma of hot bread being taken from the oven! I love to be on hand at that moment, and to put some butter on a slice, and eat it while it is still hot! It is almost a ritual at our house, for me to have a piece of hot, buttered corn bread, just moments after Frances takes it from the oven.

Some 8,000 years ago, the Swiss Lakedwellers began to pound or crush grain into a flour or meal, mix it with water, and cook it in flat cakes on hot stones. This may have been the first making of wheat bread. Probably, long before this The American Indian began to pound or crush acorns and make flat, dry cakes of bread on hot stones. Acorn bread was used widely across the Earth (where there were acorns) for thousands of years before the agriculture era began. The evidence indicates that acorn bread use began to wane around the time of Christ. I would attribute this decline to smell and taste, and the increasing availability of grains, and the aroma

Celebration of Jesus, The Bread of Life, with many kinds of bread, with the Congrgation of Pelham United Methodist Church!

and taste of grain bread, especially while it is still hot.

Bread is and has been for some eight or ten thousand years an universal food. It was and is of such great importance, in its use and in its nutritional value, that it became known as The Staff of Life. Bread is a prime source of the high-energy, fiber-rich complex carbohydrates nutritionists recommend. (Jack Denton Scott - "Our Daily Bread", Reader's Digest, Feb. 1983, p. 150).

I believe the universal appeal of bread - by smell and taste -, its nutritional value, its availability, and how easily it can be kept and carried has had much to do with it being referred to in such strong terms as - "Daily Bread". When Jesus chose to use this term in the prayer He taught His disciples, He was using the word- Bread-to refer to or mean all the nutritional values or food in general, that helps to sustain our physical lives. Cruden's Concordance says the word, "Bread", also means, "All things necessary to this life." We use the term, "The Breaking of Bread," to mean the eating of a meal. Mr. Webster, in speaking of bread says that it also means, food in general. In an article, "The World's Bread and Butter", in The Book of Knowledge, the writer says, "Bread is an excellent food, our best and cheapest source of food energy..." And, "Bread and butter, or bread and milk make a perfect food." (5), (6), (7)

The term - Bread-has taken on the additional meaning, apart from food, of making a living, our jobs, and even money. I suppose that this may, in part, be the influence of the ancient bartering system. The writer in The Encyclopedia Britannica says, "Since they had no coined money until the late Iron Age, the ancient Egyptians paid workmen and officials in grain, loaves, and beer." I remember commenting on my early experience of the paper mill smell in the Childersburg area, and the people responding, "It smells like bread and butter to me." That smell was related to their means of livelihood. (8), (9)

One of the great stories of Bread is that of God providing, "Manna from Heaven", for Moses and the Children of Israel, on their journey from slavery and bondage in Egypt to Freedom, and to become a great Nation under God, in The Promised Land! In Exodus, the 16th chapter, we are given the account of this miraculous intervention of God, in providing physical sustenance for these former slaves, as they made their journey across the great wilderness to become Israel - 'The People of God.'

To the Jew, steeped in the Mosaic Tradition, Jesus says, "I am The Manna from Heaven." And to all mankind, Jesus says, "I am The Bread of Life." I believe that Jesus chose to use this word - Bread - as a Symbol of His Life, and of His Mission to Save and Sustain Life - because of the importance of bread, in sustaining physical life, and because of its universal nature and appeal. (10)

The term - Breaking Bread - in its larger context means the eating of a meal. There is surely, no more beautiful picture of the family, than that of a family around the table, joyfully and lovingly sharing in the eating of a meal together! I believe, that Jesus chose the term, "Daily Bread", to also hallow that Family Fellowship about the table. Within 'The Family Circle', no place and no ritual or tradition can be so meaningful, so life enriching, and life sustaining, as 'The Family Breaking Bread Together'! This is a place to share about how your day has been. Children need encouragement and affirmation, instead of criticisms, we all do. Each family needs to recognize the vast possibilities and strengths to be derived from the family breaking bread together! The Church also needs a 'Vision' of that Image - of 'Breaking Bread Together as Brothers and Sisters in Christ' - for Unity and Oneness and Strength, and as a much needed witness to the community and world.

Jesse Owens was the winner of 4 Gold Medals at The 1936 Olympics in Berlin, Germany. He, thereby, became a world known and honored athlete. He was a boyhood neighbor of my Father's family at Oakville, in Lawrence County, Alabama, during the period from about 1900 to about 1915. One of the strongest and most important words that Jesse Owens used in telling his story of breaking 4 world records in one day, and then representing The United States of America at the Olympics in Berlin, and winning 4 Gold Medals was about the strength he received from his family - 'Breaking Bread Together' - in those boyhood days in Oakville, Alabama. (11)

Out of my Faith Journey - I urge each of you to establish such a 'Family Tradition of Breaking Bread Together.' Develop it in the joyful Sharing of your lives, hopes, and dreams, guard it jealously, and The Lord will Bless and Hallow it! And, from such, 'Breaking of Bread', great Blessings and Strengths for Living will be derived for each life! 'The Breaking of Bread Together' about the table, as a family, in church fellowships, and about The Altar in Holy Communion or in a Love Feast, can be a great Source of many great Spiritual Blessings and Strengths for living our daily lives victoriously!

Now, The Lord Jesus Christ raised the meaning of Bread to Sacramental, in taking it as The Symbol of His Life laid down for us He is indeed, 'The Manna from Heaven' - from God! He is 'The Bread of Life'! As we receive Him into our lives, He Redeems, Renews, Strengthens, and gives New Life and Eternal Life! (12)

There are many different kinds of bread on our chancel today - some 20 kinds in fact, representing many of the important cultures of the world across the ages. After the benediction, you are invited to come about the chancel, and 'Let's Break Bread Together!' This will, undoubtedly, be a unique experience for many of you today - we hope it will be a very 'Special Blessing'! This Bread will most likely be a delight to share and taste. It will satisfy physical hunger, and give us renewed physical vigor and vitality. But, our primary concern is to offer you, 'Jesus - The Bread of Life'! Partake of Him - Feast on Him - that He may nourish and sustain you today and forevermore!

And, Now, I invite you to come about the chancel - with The Assembled, Worshipping Community of Faith - and share in a 'Love Feast' - with 3 great emphasis: 1) Break Bread Together in Grateful Celebration of The Love of God! 2) Break Bread Together in Celebration of the privilege of being part of The Family of God - The Community of Faith - Brothers and Sisters in Christ! 3) Break Bread Together in Grateful Celebration and Thanksgiving unto God for His unspeakable Gift of Jesus - The Bread of Eternal Life! Amen and Amen!

(This Message was used in a Celebration of Worship at Pelham United Methodist Church during my pastorate there 1988-1992.)

WE STAND TODAY ON HOLY GROUND

Exodus 3:1-6; Acts 7:31-34; I Peter 2:1-10

Surely, much of the focus of our minds today is on The Church, and what it means to us, or can and should mean to us! Such thoughts ought to 1st, move us to declare with the Psalmist - "O Lord, our Lord, how Majestic is Thy Name in all the earth!" Truly, "Great is the Lord, and greatly to be praised in the City of our God, in the mountain of His Holiness." For, The Lord is Good, His Mercy is everlasting, and His Faithfulness is unto every generation, Blessed be The Name of The Lord for ever and for evermore!"

Our Lord is to be Praised for He has given us The Church - but, oh, at what a cost!

Surely, the thought of The Church brings many images to mind - a very special place - 'A Special Fellowship of Love and Faith' - a place that has become Sacred because of the experience of The Grace of God. Thereby, for many here today, this place has truly become Holy Ground!

Such a thought, undoubtedly, moved and inspired the poet, who wrote, "The Church in The Wildwood." There are many images in that hymn that speak to our inner being - such as - 'no spot so dear', 'the little brown church in the vale', 'the peaceful valley', 'the ringing bell' - en route here today, I came by Courtland United Methodist Church, where I remember hearing the ringing of the church bell, as my boyhood family walked three miles (from about 1 mile north - west of General Joe Wheeler Home), out a dirt road and down the highway to Courtland to church and Sunday School. (1)

Such images, remind us of Moses' experience of the 'Burning Bush' - and it became 'Holy Ground' for him, for there he experienced the Presence, and Grace, and Call of God. He would never be the same again, for out of this experience of God's Grace, his life would reach far, and touch, and influence his people and his generation; but, it would also impact our generation, and to the ends of the earth. For Moses, this experience meant a clear Call, and a strong claim of God on his life. God would be with him to guide and strengthen him in the fulfillment of the task to which he was Called. God always provides the wherewithal to do his bidding - for our God is indeed able to see us through every job and challenge that He calls us to do, or to face! And, He will do so, if we Trust Him and Obey!

Brethren, as that place - long ago, and far away - became Holy Ground for Moses, this place too has for many, many persons across the years, become Holy Ground. For many persons have here at this place, come to realize or to realize more fully, their own special need of God's Grace. And, in the acknowledgement of that need, they have experienced Redeeming Grace, and/or Sustaining Grace. Many have come here longing and hungering for inner Peace, and in the response of Faith, they have experienced those blessed words of Jesus, "Thy sins be forgiven thee, go in Peace." And out of such experience of Grace, we have risen to Praise God from Whom all blessings flow, and to declare, and to show forth through our lives, Praise and Thanksgiving for God's Goodness and Mercy to our generation - Blessed be The Name of The Lord our God! (2)

This Place has become Holy Ground, because here in Worship, Prayer, and Meditation, many have heard The Call of God in their lives. Across the years, many have gathered here out of the trials and tribulations - and out of the joys and sorrows of daily life - and have here found Peace and Rest unto their souls - Just as Jesus Promised they would! Now, this rest had to do with Spiritual refreshment, and renewal, and new Strength for the living of these days! This Rest relates to that blessed word that Isaiah speaks, when he says, "They that wait upon The Lord shall renew their strength, they shall mount up with wings of eagles, they shall run and not be weary, they shall walk and not faint." Surely, where we have experienced such marvelous Grace of God, that Place has become for us - Holy Ground! Surely, this Church has been such for

The Prayer at Valley Forge. Gen. George Washington, winter 177 - 78. Copy of engraving by John C. McRae after Henry Brueckner, published 1866. (George Washington Bicentennial Commission

hundreds across the years! (3)

Such thoughts of The Church, remind us as The Discipline says, that The Church is of God, and shall be preserved to the end of time, for the Proclamation of The Gospel, for the Edification of Believers, for the due administration of The Sacraments, and for the Conversion of the world. (4)

Across the Ages, The Elders, The Church Fathers, The Inspired Writers of Scripture have called The Church, a holy and royal priesthood, a chosen generation, a holy nation, the Laos, the People of God, the Koinonia, The Community of Faith, and The Body of Christ. All these great terms of The Faith, remind us of the nature and purpose of The Church of The Living God. The dominant note in all these terms is servant - and Charles Wesley, inspired Hymn Writer, speaks to this in: 'to serve the present age, our calling to fulfill - ' And, The Model ever before us is: Jesus, girded with a towel - serving! He is our model, and He is saying to us, "I came not to be ministered unto, but to minister and give My Life.' And, through His Church, He Calls us to do the same. (5), (6), (7)

Some years ago, I walked through Valley Forge National Park. During that walk, the thought occurred to me, that that ground had been hallowed - made forever sacred by the sacrifice of those noble patriots, who gave so deeply of their lives and fortunes, for the birth of Freedom and Democracy, that we hold so dear and precious. My brethren, this place also, has been made Holy Ground, by the Love and Commitment of many Saints of God, who were 'Pillars of this Church', whose Dedication was an Offering unto God, and should forever be an inspiration and challenge to our lives. I found myself thinking of many of those Saints of The Lord and of The Church, such as Tom Queen, with whom I was privileged to walk, worship, and serve in SEJANAM, on behalf of Native American Brothers and Sisters. And as a Great Cloud of Witnesses they surround us today, with love and Precious Memories, and they Cheer us on to Victory!

They would call us to 'turn our eyes upon Jesus - The Author and Finisher of our Faith! And, they would urge us to renew our commitment to The Race that has been set before us, and to be Faithful, that we too might win The Crown of Eternal Life! And, that we too might soon join with them in The Father's House, world without end, Amen and Amen!

OUR GOD IS ABLE

Ephesians 3:14-21, & Jude 1:24-25

Let us do a little experiment as an illustration, to ponder this morning. In our imagination, let us turn or spin a globe of the world, and focus in on the most noted and the most significant inventions and achievements of the human family. Let us note those in the areas of music, art, literature, health, industry, communication, travel, agriculture, philosophy, and political thought, etc.

Surely, in doing such an experiment, we begin to realize that these significant achievements are scattered all across the earth, and come from the various parts of the human family. Today, most of our lives are touched and enriched by contributions of various members of the human family, from literally all across the world. Truly, as The Apostle Paul says, "We are debtors to many people." Truly, today, no person lives or dies unto themselves - as the poet so fittingly says..."No man is an island."

Now, as we do such an overview of man's noteworthy work or achievements, we need to be very careful, lest we find ourselves in awe - or in fact, worshipping with.... "Oh, how great man is!"

We need to learn from The Apostle Peter, as recorded in Acts 10:26, not to be overly impressed or awed by any fellow human being. You see, there were those who were going to bow down to The Apostle Peter, as though he were a god - which he was not! And, the Apostle being an humble and noble man, told them to get up and stand on your feet, for I too am but a man. Too often, some seek after such following, and to play as a god with other people's lives. (1)

Mankind has indeed made some great discoveries and achievements. One of the greatest discoveries man has ever made or will ever make, is that whatever of significance that he ever learns, or achieves is by 'The Design, and through The Grace of God'! And, with that discovery, there also comes the dawning consciousness, that of man's own design or self-will, his personal life and community life - even in the church - can get awfully messed up. In fact, tensions and inter-relational conflicts often indicate that someone is trying to play god, and do it their own way, instead of humbly and prayerfully seeking God's way. In truly seeking God's Will and Way, we will bring Harmony, Unity, and Spiritual strength into the 'Community of Faith'. One of the greatest Principles of our Faith as Christians is that we should make key decisions only by or under the guidance of God. For, by God's Design, it will be blessed and it will bring forth Fruit and Harmony!

God did not design our personal or community lives in such a way, that we could successfully manage on our own. It is beyond our ability to manage life on our own. It must be under the direction and guidance of The Holy Spirit, if we would know inner peace, and harmony in our relationships, and reach toward our God intended potential, and bear fruit, as we ought, to the Glory of God!

The greatest, most significant moment, in any life, is that moment when there dawns, at last, the consciousness of the Reality, and Greatness, and Goodness of God! And, out of this awareness, there comes that unconquerable Faith - 'Our God is Able'!

Maybe you ask, 'Able to do what?' If we had the capacity to grasp the vastness and order of this universe, then we might be able realistically to begin to think and talk about how big, how Great, and how Mighty our God truly is! Most of us are like the proverbial Texan, we are much impressed by the size of Texas - or by what we have done - or by the power we wield. If only we could back off in a sense, and truly see the universe, and life - and the size and significance of our power in it - from God's point of view. 1st, we would be overwhelmed - 2ndly, we just might be humbled, and get our feet on the earth - God's earth - and bow in humble submission to God!

We sometimes, stand in awe of some genius and think how much they have attained or achieved, while some of the truly great among them, like Louis Pasteur, remind us that they have attained so very little of what is there to learn or to attain, or to accomplish.

On the other hand, and far more important, when we truly see God, as He is - Father-God-Creator of the universe - Caring for His own, surely, we are truly overwhelmed and awed by His Great Love, and by what He can and will do for us - each and all! Surely, we are reminded by the hymn - "It is no secret what God can do, what He has done for others, He will do for you!"

Our God is Able to save to the utmost - all who put their trust in Him! When man looks honestly in his heart and life, one thing he knows for sure - the truth of God's Word, that, "We are all sinners, that we have all sinned and come short of the glory of God.: Knowing our own bent to sinning, it is natural, with Nicodemus, to have some doubts, about how this, 'born again' experience, can be - how we can truly be changed, and become new creatures in Christ Jesus. The Good News of The Gospel - is that by The Grace of God - through Faith in Jesus Christ - we can be born anew and we can be changed! And the testimony of millions, of those who have trusted in Jesus, is that our God is Able to Save - for God was and is in Christ reconciling the world unto Himself! And Jesus, The Christ of God, is Able to Save all those who believe in Him, repent of their sin, and say Yes unto God with all their heart. That means 'to be Obedient' unto the moving of The Spirit of The Lord. To use the old Spiritual - I'm gonna sing, when The Spirit says sing - Pray - Work. Jesus is indeed Able to Save even unto the utmost! (2), (3)

Look at Simon Peter, and especially at Saul of Tarsus. Peter was so tempestuous and so undependable, that Jesus spoke of him as shifting sand or pebbles. Many would have considered him hopeless, but, Jesus did not! Jesus chose him, as a Follower, and to become an Apostle! What a symbol of Hope that becomes for us, and for all mankind. (4)

Then, consider Saul. He was so caught up in self-centeredness or self-will. Saul was so caught up in the work of Judaism. He was zealous for God - but, only in his own way. He could hate with the vilest of the world, and he could run rough shod over those who did not agree with him. Saul's zeal was completely out of touch with God's Spirit. To some, Saul was hopelessly lost, but, even more tragic, to many, he was alright, just like he was - zealous Pharisee - arrogant - do it my way - and it did not matter to him who it hurt.

And, in the very midst of the conflict and tension and turmoil, Saul cried out, "Oh, wretched man that I am, who will save me from this death?" When there is such inner turmoil, there can't help but be turmoil in our relationships. But, Thanks be unto God, in and through Christ, Saul could be changed - and miracle of miracles - he was! And, he could and did become the number one proponent of 'Unity and Harmony and Teamwork in the Body of Christ in The New Testament and in The Church! He learned the meaning of concern for others - 'to sit where they sit.' (5)

Our God is Able to lead us from Victory unto Victory! It is the nature of life to have to face difficulties. The writer of The Book of Hebrews, who knew so much of life, and of The Faith, needed to live triumphantly, says in Hebrews 2:18, "Our God through Jesus is able to succor - to sustain those who are tempted and tried. He is able to lead them through the dark night of the soul. Daniel speaks out of the fiery furnace experience, to a most difficult hour, in words of such Great Faith - 'Our God is Able to Deliver us!' (6)

He can lead to Victory in the challenge before any Church. He has sustained His People through the dark days of slavery in Egypt, and in the almost impossible journey to The Promised Land. God has sustained and led many of His believing children from bondage on to The Promised Land of Freedom and Opportunity! God always sustains His People on the journey to which He calls them - or as they endeavor to do the work which He calls them to do and entrusts to their hands, Our Promise Land is, in part, wherever God Calls us to be in Ministry and to be about The Lord's Work!

Our God is Able to sustain us even through the Valley of Death, and over the chilling waters of Jordan, unto The Father's House! The Apostle Paul, facing persecution and martyrdom, said, with victorious confidence, "He is Able to keep, that which I have committed to Him against that day." Paul, after his Damascus Road experience, of Redeeming Grace, invested his life in The Kingdom of God, and in The Spirit of Jesus, and became confident that he would draw great returns on that investment for all Eternity! Thanks be unto God! (7)

David, in Psalms 23, speaks through a Great Faith, to many, Many millions of believing hearts and lives - to our 'inner being', "Yea though I walk through the valley of death, I will fear no evil, for Thou art with me!" God cares for His own! Through Jesus, He Shepherds us! (8)

Best of all is, He who walked through that 'Valley of Death; - so triumphantly at Calvary for us - will Now - as The Good Shepherd walk it with us! Thanks be unto God! My Brothers and Sisters - Our God Is Able!

And, Jude, in the closing of his little book, says in great Faith and Confidence, "Now unto Him who is Able...... " (9)

Let us Go Forth and Share The Good News to all that Our God is Able! Will you be a Joyful and Willing Witness or Bearer of that Positive and Triumphant Faith? Give your life as such - - Now, and Forevermore unto God, for He is Able - unto the Utmost! Amen & Amen!

'LIVE IN HARMONY"

The Story I Love to Tell - often - is how the American Indian put much emphasis on, 'Live in Harmony.'

Where and when did the concept of: 'Live in Harmony with the Great Spirit, with Mother Earth, with all living things', come alive in and among The American Indian? So far as I know, or could find out through research, there is no legend of its beginning. I have sought it for many years, in a great deal of research, travel, and sharing in exchange of views. I am convinced that it gradually evolved , somewhat as a jonquil does - very slowly it pokes its head out of the darkness of the inner earth, into the sunshine and gentle showers - and after many days of growth and development - a head or bud begins to develop. Then, after what seems an eternity, especially, if you have been too anxiously and too closely watching - finally - it begins to slowly open forth to all its wonder, and glorious beauty! And, maybe that is as The Great Spirit - The Creator planned in Wisdom that it should be!

Surely, as we ponder this great concept - 'Live in Harmony' - we sense, our inner being affirms that it is right, that it is as life should be lived, as human relationships should be, it is surely as The Great Spirit designed it to be!

Therefore, let us above all - teach the world to sing - dance - sit together - in 'Great Circles of Life in The Spirit' - listening to one another, seeking to understand each other, and, learning to walk together and work together - in perfect Harmony! Then-there shall be 'Peace on Earth Goodwill among men - even as God, through the Ages has been leading us to do! Let us Now and henceforth, Trust and Obey! (1)

A Ministry of Love of The John Franklin Phillips Family across a half century. We trust that your life has been Blessed and Enriched in the Sharing!

Notes

'A GREAT LESSON IN HISTORY

1) Morgan, Henry Lewis, Ancient Society, New York:Henry Holt, c-1877.
2) Schoolcraft, Henry R., History of The Indian Tribes of North America, New York:Lippincott, c-1851, 1857.

MY FATHERS, WE HAVE SOME UNFINISHED BUSINESS TO DO.

1) National Geographic Society, World of The American Indian, Washington, D. C., c-1974, 1979, pages 11, 14, 16, 18, 20, 22.

'THE GREEN CORN DANCE'

1) Burt, Jesse, and Ferguson, Robert B., Indians of The Southeast: Then and Now, Nashville:Abingdon Press, c-1973, page 70. (Used by permission.)
2) Ibid, page 71.
3) Hudson, Charles, The Southeastern Indians, Knoxville: The University Press, c-1976, pages 366-375.
4) Reader's Digest, America's Fascinating Indian Heritage, Pleasantville, N. Y.:The Reader's Digest Association, Inc., c-1978, page 102.
5) Reader's Digest, Through Indian Eyes, Pleasantville, New York A Montreal, c-1995, The Reader's Digest Association, Inc., page 39.
6) Burt, Jesse, and Ferguson, Robert B., The Indians of The Southeast: Then and Now, Nashville:Abingdon Press, c-1973, (used by permission.) pages 68-69.
7) Reader's Digest, America's Fascinating Indian Heritage, Pleasantville, New York, R Montreal:The Reader's Digest Association, Inc.,c-1978, page 132.
8) Burt, Jesse, k Ferguson, Robert B., Indians of The Southeast: Then and Now, Nashville:Abingdon Press, c-1973, page 59, (used by permission.)
9) Phillips, John Franklin, The Indian Heritage of Americans, Birmingham: The Birmingham Printing & Publishing Co., for American Indian Books, c-1984, 3rd printing, Oct, 199O, page 14.
10) Clinton, Hillary Rodham, It Takes a Village, New York: Touchstone of Simon and Schuster, Inc., c- 1996, pages 12-15.
11) Reader's Digest, Through Indian Eyes, Pleasantville, New York 4 Montreal,: The Reader's Digest Association, Inc., c-1995, page 39. (Used with permission.)
12) Phillips, John Franklin, The American Indian in Alabama and The Southeast, Nashville:Parthenon Press, for American Indian Books, c-1986, page 29.
13) Hudson, Charles, The Southeastern Indians, Knoxville: The University Press, c-l976, pages 374-375.
14) Phillips, John Franklin, The Indian Heritage of Americans, Birmingham: The Birmingham Printing and Publishing Co., for American Indian Books, c-1984, 3rd. printing, Oct., 1990, page 14.

'BURY THE HATCHET'

1) 2 Corinthians 5:18-19, (Scripture quotations are &from the Revised Standard Version of the Bible, copyright 1946, 1952, 1971 by the Division of Christian Education of the National Council of the Churches of Christ in USA. Used by permission. All rights reserved.)
2) Ibid, Matthew 5:24. (same as 1)
3) Hendrickson, Robert, The Facts on File Encyclopedia of Word and Phrase Origins, c-1987, by Robert Hendrickson, (reprinted by permission of Facts on File, Inc.)
4) Longfellow, Henry Wadsworth, The Legend of Hiawatha, 1855
5) Schoolcraft, Henry R., The History of The Indian Tribes of North America, New York:Lippincott
6) Weatherford, Jack McIver, Native Roots-How The Indian Enriched America, New York:Crown Publishing Ca., Inc., c-1991, pages 286, 287.
7) Josephy, Alvin M. Jr., The Patriot Chiefs- Chronicle of American Indian Leadership, New York: The Viking Press, c-1961, pages 22-23.
8) Wallace, Paul A. W., White Roots of Peace, The Iroquois Book of Life, by Paul Wallace, Illustrated by John Kahionhes Fadden, Foreword by Chief Leon Shennandoah, Message &am Chief Sidney I Hill, Epilogue by John Mohawk, Philadelphia: The University of Pennsylvania Press, c-l946, Reprinted by Santa Fe:Clear Light Publishers, pages 25-28.

'THE SACRED PIPE'

National Geographic Society, Editors, The World of The American Indian, c-1974, 1979, pages 11, 14, 16, 18, 20, 22.

'A CHOICE OF LIFE MADE - A DIRECTION OF LIFE SET'

1) Phillips, John Franklin, The American Indian in Alabama and The Southeast, Nashville:Parthenon Press for American Indian Books., c-1986, pages 52-53.
2) 1bid, page 53.

3) Pickett, Albert James, History of Alabama, Birmingham:Birmingham Book and Magazine Co., Republished 1962, pages 75, 78, 397, 399.
4) Edmunds, R. David, Edited by, American Indian Leaders:Studies in Diversity, Lincoln, Ne.:The University of Nebraska Press, (&from a chapter by Michael D. Green, page 55.)
5) Phillips, John Franklin, The American Indian in Alabama and The Southeast, Nashville:Parthenon Press for American Indian Books c-1986, page 54.
6) Weatherford, Jack McIver, Indian Givers-How The Indians of The Americas Transformed The World, New York:Crown Publishers, Inc., c-1988, page 156.

'FREEDOM AND SELF-DETERMINATION'

1) King, Martin Luther, Jr., The Reverend, Dr., quote from his sermon - "I Have a Dream" - preached to a vast congregation gathered on The quadrangle in Washington, D. C., at The March for jobs and Freedom held in the Nation's Capitol on August 28, 1963. Permission granted by the King Estate's literary agent, Writer's House.
2) Schoolcraft, Henry R., History of The Indian Tribes of North America, New York:Lippincott, c-1851, 1857
3) Wallace, Paul A. W., White Roots of Peace, The Iroquois Book of Life by Paul Wallace, Illustrated by John Kahionhes Fadden, Foreword by Chief Leon Shennandoah, Message &from Chief Sidney I Hill, Epilogue by John Mohawk, Philadelphia: The University of Pennsylvania Press, c-1946, Reprinted by Santa Fe:Clear Light Publishers, c-1994, page 94.
4) Johansen, Bruce E., Forgotten Founders - How The American Indian Helped Shape Democracy. Harvard and Boston: The Harvard Common Press, c-l982, pages xv, 14, 120.

'GREAT IMAGES - SYMBOLS - CONCEPTS OF THE AMERICAN INDIAN'

1) Colden, Cadwallader, History of The Five Nations Depending on The Province of New York in American 1727, 1747, Ithaca, N.Y.:Cornell University Press, c-1958, page xx.
2) Weatherford, Jack McIver, Indian Givers-How The Indians of The Americas Transformed The World, New York:Crown Publishers, Inc., c-l988, pages 145, 147, 149.
3) Weatherford, Jack McIver, Native Roots-How The Indians Enriched America, New York:Crown Publishers, Inc., c-1991, pages 287-288.
4) Wallace, Paul A. W., White Roots of Peace, The Iroquois Book of Life by Paul Wallace, Illustrated by john Kahionhes Fadden, Foreword by Chief Leon Shennandoah, Message &from Chief Sidney I Hill, Epilogue by John Mohawk, Philadelphia: The University of Pennsylvania Press, c-1946, Reprinted by Santa Fe:Clear Light Publishers, c-l994, pages 108-112.

'SEQUOYAH'

1) "Indian Chiefs", by Lynne Deur, page 35, copyright 1972, by Lerner Publications. Used by permission of the publishers. All rights reserved.
la) Mooney. James, Historical Sketch of The Cherokee. Chicago:Aldine Publishing Co., c-1975, by Smithsonian Institute Press, page 99.
2) O'Donnell, James H. 3rd., Southern Indians in The American Revolution, Knoxville: The University of Tennessee Press, c-1973, page 55.
3) Walker, Rickey "Butch", Warrior Mountain Folklore, printed by The Lawrence County Schools Indian Education Program, page 14.
4) McDonald, William "Bill" Lindsey, Lore of The River-The Shoals of Long Ago, Published by Florence Historical Board, c-1989, page 31.
5) Porter, C. Fayne, Our Indian Heritage, Philadelphia:Chilton Book Co., c-1964, page 55.
6) Malone, Henry Thompson, Cherokees of The Old South, Athens: The University of Georgia Press, c- 1956, pages 155-156.
7) "Indian Chiefs" by Lynne Deur, page 37. Copyright 1972 by Lerner Publications. Used by permission of the publishers. All rights reserved.
8) Mooney, James, Historical Sketch of The Cherokee, Chicago:Aldine Publishing Co., c-1975 by The Smithsonian Institute Press, page 227.
9) Porter, C. Fayne, Our Indian Heritage, Philadelphia:Chilton Book Co., c-1964. Pages 54-55.
10) Journal of Cherokee Studies, John Howard Payne, "Notable Persons in Cherokee History:Sequoyah or George Gist", c-1977, page 388.
11) Porter, C. Fayne, Our Indian Heritage, Philadelphia:Chilton Book Co., c-1964, pages 59-61.
lla) Malone, Henry Thompson, Cherokees of The Old South, Athens:University of Georgia Press, c-l956, page 156.
12) "Indian Chiefs", by Lynne Deur, page 39. Copyright 1972 by Lerner Publications. Used by permissions of the publisher. All rights reserved.
13) Mooney, James, Historical Sketch of The Cherokee, Chicago:Aldine Publishing Co., c-1975 by Smithsonian Institute Press, page 102.
14) Hudson, Charles, The Southeastern Indians, Knoxville:University of Tennessee Press, c-1976, page 25.

14a) Josephy, Alvin M. Jr., The Indian Heritage of America, New York:Knopf, c-1968, page 108.
14b) Reader's Digest, Through Indian Eyes, Pleasantville, N.Y.: The Reader's Digest Association, Inc., c- 1995, page 69.
14c) National Geographic Society, The World of The American Indian, c-1974, 1979, Washington, D. C., page 151.
15) Noley, Homer, The First White Frost, Nashville:Abingdon Press, c-1991, page 126, (used with permission.)
16) Foreman, Grant, The Five Civilized Tribes, Norman:University of Oklahoma Press, c-1934, page 371.
16a) Phillips, John Franklin, The American Indian in Alabama and The Southeast, Nashville:Parthenon Press for American Indian Books, c-1986, pages 42, 43.

'THE GREAT COUNCIL FIRE'

1) Owen, Marie, Our State-Alabama, Birmingham:Birmingham Printing and Publishing Co, c-l927, page 79.
2) Phillips, John Franklin, The American Indian in Alabama and The Southeast, Nashville:Parthenon Press for American Indian Books, c-1986, pages 60-61.
3) Ibid, page 64.
4) Owen, Marie, Our State-Alabama, Birmingham:Birmingham Printing and Publishing Co.,c-1927, page 79.

'THE GREAT CIRCLES OF LIFE'

1) Editors, Native Peoples Magazine, The National Museum of The American Indian, Smithsonian Institute, pages 26-32.
2) Wallace, Paul A. W., White Roots of Peace, The Iroquois Book of Life by Paul Wallace, Illustrated by John Kahionhes Fadden. Foreword by Chief Leon Shenandoah, Message &from Chief Sidney I Hill, Epilogue by John Mohawk, Philadelphia: The University of Pennsylvania Press, c-1946. Reprinted by Santa Fe:Clear Light Publishers, pages 25-28,

'DEGANAWIDAH - MAN OF GREAT VISION'

1) Schoolcraft, Henry R., The History of The Indian Tribes of North America, New York:Lippincott, c-1851, 1857, page
2) Morgan, Henry Lewis, Ancient Society, New York:Henry Holt, c-1877-page
3) Schoolcraft, Henry R., The hHistory of The Indian Tribes of north America, New York:Lippincott, c- 1851, 1857, page

'THE GREAT WHITE PINE OF PEACE'

1) Weatherford, Jack McIver, Native Roots-How The Indian Enriched America, New York:Crown c-1991, page 286.
2) Johansen, Bruce E., Forgotten Founders, Boston: The Harvard Common Press, c-l982, pages 23-24.
3) Josephy, Alvin M. Jr., 500 Nations-An Illustrated History of North American Indians, New York:Alfred A. Knopf, c-1994, page 49.
4) Wallace, Paul A. W., White Roots of Peace - as excerpted from White Roots of Peace, The Iroquois Book of Life by Paul Wallace with a Foreword by Chief Leon Shenandoah. C-1994, reprinted by Santa Fe:Clear Light Publishers. www.Clear Light Books.Com, page 94.
5) Weatherford, Jack McIver, Native Roots-How The Indian Enriched America, Hew York:Crown, c-1991, page 287.

'HIAWATHA'

1) Schoolcraft, Henry R., History of The Indian Tribes of North America, New York:Lippincott, c-1851, 1857.
2) Josephy, Alvin M. Jr., 500 Nations, New York:Alfred A. Knopf, c-1994, page 48.
3) Josephy, Alvin M. Jr., The Patriot Chiefs, New York: The Viking Press, c-1958, page 20.
3a) Porter, C. Fayne, Our Indian heritage - Profiles of 12 Great Leaders, Philadelphia:Chilton Book Co. c- 1964, page 11.
4) Schoolcraft, Henry R., history of The Indian Tribes of North American New York:Lippincott, c-1851, 1857, Volume 5, page 157.
5) Josephy, Alvin M. Jr., The Patriot Chiefs - A Chronicle of The American Indian Resistance, New York: Viking Penguin, c-1958, 1993, page 22.
6) Josephy, Alvin M. Jr., 500 Nations, New York:Alfred A. Knopf, c-1994, pages 49, 17, 21.
7) Reader's Digest, Editors, America's Fascinating Indian Heritage, Pleasantville, N. Y.:Reader's Digest Association, Inc., c-1978, page 12.
8) Schoolcraft, Henry R., History of The Indian Tribes of North America, c-1851, 1857, Volume 5, page 162.
9) Ibid, page 162.
10) Ibid, page 163.
11) Fleming, Alden O., Manabozho-The Indian's Story of Hiawatha, c-1938, page 87.

'NATIVE AMERICAN SPIRITUALITY'

1) Pickett, Albert James, History of Alabama, Birmingham, Al.:Birmingham Book and Magazine Co., Reprint, 1962, page 71.
la) Hudson, Charles, The Southeastern Indians, Knoxville: The University of Tennessee Press, c-1976, page 122.
2) Adair, James, History of The American Indian, New York:Promontory Press, c-1930, page 38.

3) Ibid, pages 24, 435.
4) Isaiah 40:31, Scripture quotations are from the Revised Standard Version of the Bible, copyright 1946, 1952, 1971 by the Division of Christian Education of the National Council of the Churches of Christ in the USA. Used by permission. All rights reserved.
5) Adair, James, History of The American Indian, New York:Promontory Press, c-l930, page 105.
5a) Schoolcraft, Henry R., History of The Indian Tribes of North America, c-1851, 1857, Volume 5, page 267.
6) National Geographic Society, Editors, World of The American Indian, Washington, D. C., c-1974, 1979, page 10, (Picture of Pipe Communion with The Great Spirit.).
7) Hudson, Charles, The Southeastern Indians, Knoxville: The University of Tennessee Press, c-1976, page 367.
7a) Phillips, John Franklin, The American Indian in Alabama and The Southeast, Nashville:Parthenon Press for American Indian Books, c-1986, pages 26, 28.
8) National Geographic Society, Editors, The World of The American Indian, Washington, D. C., c-1974, 1979, pages 11, 14, 16, 18, 20, 22.
9) From Presentation in The Oconaluftee Living Indian Village, Cherokee, North Carolina.

'BIRTH OF THE HAU-DE-NO-SAU-NEE OR LEAGUE OF IROQUOIS NATIONS'

1) Schoolcraft, Henry R., History of The Indian Tribes of North America, New York:Lippincott, c-1851, 1857, Volume 5, page 638.
2) Josephy, Alvin M. Jr., 500 Nations, New York:Alfred A. Knopf, c-1994, page 44.
3) Weatherford, Jack McIver, Indian Givers-How The Indians of The Americas Transformed the World, New York:Crown Publishers, Inc., c-1988, page 135.
4) Schoolcraft, Henry R., History of The Indian Tribes of North America, New York:Lippiancott, c-1851, 1857, Volume, page
5) Reader's Digest, America's Fascinating Indian Heritage, Pleasantville, N. Y.: The Reader's Digest Association, Inc., c-1978, page 126.
6) Marquis, Arnold, Guide to America s Indians: Ceremonial, Reservations, and Museums, Norman:University of Oklahoma Press, c-1974, page 49.
7) Porter, C. Fayne, Our Indian Heritage-Profiles of 12 Great Leaders, Philadelphia:Chilton Book Co., c-1964, page 11.
8) Notable Native Americans, Editor, Sharon Malinowski, page 193, Gale Research, Inc., an International Thomson Publishing Co., c-1995.
9) Morgan, Lewis Henry, Ancient Society, New York:Henry Holt, c-1877, page 112.
9a) Morgan, Lewis Henry, League of The Hau-no-sau-nee or Iroquois, 1851, New York:Dodd, Mead, and Co., c-1902, page
10) Morgan, Lewis Henry, Ancient Society, New York:Henry Holt, c-l877, page 114.
11) Ibid, pages 114-115.
12) Ibid, page 119.
13) Waldman, Carl, Encyclopedia of Native American Tribes, New York:Facts on File, c-1988, page 170,
14) Josephy, Alvin M. Jr., The Patriot Chiefs, New York: The Viking Press, c-1958, page 25.
14a) As excerpted from White Roots of Peace, The Iroquois Book of Life by Paul Wallace with a Foreword by Chief Leon Shenandoah. C-1994, Santa Fe:Clear Light Publishers, www. ClearLight Books.Com page 108.

'CHARACTERISTICS OF THE AMERICAN INDIAN'

1) Christopher Columbus in a report to Queen Isabella of How the Indians received them, from Reader's Digest, Through Indian Eyes, Pleasantville, New York, c-1995, page 43.
2) McNickle, D'Arcy, They Came Here First: The Epic of the American Indian, Philadelphia:Lippincott Co., c-1949, page 92.
3) Viole, Herman J., After Columbus-The Smithsonian Chronicle of The North American Indians, c-1990, New York:Orion Books, page 27.
4) Wallace, Paul A. W., Pennsylvania-Seed of A Nation, New York A Evanston:Harper A Row, c-1962, pages 41, 16.
4a) As excerpted from White Roots of Peace, The Iroquois Book of Life by Paul Wallace with a Foreword by Chief Leon Shenandoah. C-1994, Santa Fe:Clear Light Publishers, www.Clear Light Books.Com, page 14.
5) Lawson, John, History of Carolina,
6) Pickett, Albert James, History of Alabama, Birmingham:Birmingham Book and Magazine Co., reprinted in 1962, page 69.
7) Cohen, Felix, "Americanizing the White Man", (article in) The American Scholar 21:2 (1952), page 181.

'PROFILE OF A CHIEF'

1) Josephy, Alvin M. Jr., Edited by, America in 1492, the World of the Indian Peoples before the arrival of Columbus, (in a chapter - American Frontiers, by Francis Jennings, page 334.) New York:Alfred A. Knopf, Inc., c-1991, by Newberry Library, & 1992 Distributed by Random House.

2) Colden, Cadwallader, History of The Five Indian Nations, which are Dependent on the Province of New York in America. (2 vols.; New York:New Amsterdam Book Co., 1902), pages xvii-xix.
3) La Farge, Oliver, A Pictorial History of The American Indian, New York:Crown Publishers, Inc., c-1956, revised & c-1974 by the estate of Oliver La Farge, Alvin M. Josephy, Jr., &, Crown Publishers, Inc., pages 52, 55.
4) Ibid, page 98.
5) Wallace, Paul A. W., Pennsylvania-Seed of A Nation, New York:Harper & Row, c-1962, pages 26-27.
6) Porter, C. Fayne, Our Indian Heritage-Profiles of 12 Great Leaders, Philadelphia:Chilton Book Co., c-1964. Page 14.
6a) Roland, Albert, Great Indian Chiefs, New York:Crowell-Collier Press, c-1966, by The MacMillian Co., New York, page 20.
7) Josephy, Alvin M. Jr., Patriot Chiefs, New York:Viking Penguin, c-1958, 1961, 1989, page 7.
8) Phillips, John Franklin, The American Indian in Alabama and The Southeast, Nashville:Parthenon Press (for American Indian Books) c-1986, page 79.

'WILLIAM PENN - ARCHITECT OF DEMOCRACY'

1) Wallace, Paul A. W., Pennsylvania-Seed of A Nation, New York: Harper & Row, c-1962, page xiii.
2) Peare, Catherine Owens, William Penn, a Biography, Philadelphia A New York: J. B. Lippincott Co., c-1956, page 23.
3) Ibid, page 26.
3a) La Farge, Oliver, A Pictorial History of The American Indian, New York:Crown Publishers, Inc., c-1956, reprinted 1974 by the estate of Oliver La Farge, Alvin M. Josephy, Jr., and Crown Publishers Inc., c-1974, page 29.
4) Wallace, Paul A. W., Pennsylvania-Seed of a Nation, New York:Harper & Row, c-1962, page 36.
5) Ibid, page 37.
6) Ibid, page 38.
7) Ibid, page 39.
8) Ibid, page 15.
9) Josephy, Alvin M. Jr., 500 Nations-an Illustrated History of North American Indians, New York:Alfred A. Knopf, c-1994, page 235.
9a) Du Ponceau, Peter S., & Fisher, J. Francis, A Memoir on The History of The Celebrated Treaty made by William Penn with The Indians under The Elm Tree at Shackamaxon in the year 1682. Page
10) Editors, Reader's Digest, Through Indian Eyes, Pleasantville, N. Y.:Reader's Digest Association, Inc., c-1995, pages 140, 141.
11) Editors, National Geographic Society, The World of The American Indian, Washington, D. C., c-1974, 1979, page 313.
12) La Farge, Oliver, A Pictorial History of The American Indian, New York:Crown Publishers, Inc., c-1956, 1974 by the estate of Oliver La Farge, Alvin M. Josephy, Jr.,and Crown Publishers, Inc., page 78.
13) Du Ponceau, Peter S., & Fisher, J. Francis, Memoir on the History of The Celebrated Treaty made by William Penn with The Indians under The Elm Tree at Shackamaxon in the year 1682, page 147.
14) la Farge, Oliver, A Pictorial History of The American Indian, New York:Crown Publishers, Inc., c-1956, reprinted 1974 by the estate of Oliver La Farge, Alvin M. Josephy, Jr., and Crown Publishers, Inc., page 81.
15) Du Ponceau, Peter S., ' Fisher, J, Francis, A Memoir on The history of The Celebrated Treaty made by William Penn with The Indians under The Elm Tree at Shackamaxon in the year 1682, page

'TRIBUTE TO A GREAT MAN - GEORGE WASHINGTON - FATHER OF A NATION!'

1) The Book of Knowledge, The Grolier Society, Inc., New York, 1960, Volume

'FOUNDING FATHERS OF AMERICA STARING BENJAMIN FRANKLIN'

1) Wallace, Paul A. W., Pennsylvania-Seed of a Nation, New York:Harper & Row, c-1962, pages 125-126.
2) Colden, Cadwallader, The History of The Five Nations Depending on the Province of New York in America, (1727 & 1747) Ithaca, N. Y.:Cornell University Press, c-1958, page xx.
3) Weatherford, Jack McIver, Indian Givers-How The Indians of The Americas Transformed The World, New York:Crown Publishers, Inc., c-1988, page 136.
4) Johansen, Bruce E., Forgotten Founders-How The American Indian Helped Shape Democracy, Harvard & Boston: The Harvard Common Press, c-1982, pages 54, 120.
5) Bigelow, John, Editor, The Complete Works of Benjamin Franklin, c-1867, New York:Grosset & Dunlap, page 210.
5a) Koch, Adriene, Editor, The American Enlightenment-The Shaping of The American Experiment and a Free Society, New York:G. Braziller, c-1965, pages 76, 80, 138.
5b) Josephy, Alvin M. Jr., The Patriot Chiefs, New York:Viking-Penguin, c-1958, page 29.
6) Cohen, Felix S., article: "Americanizing The White Man", in The American Scholar, Winter, '51-Spring, '52, page 185.
7) Weatherford, Jack McIver, Indian Givers-How The Indian of The Americas Transformed The World, New

York:Crown Publishers, Inc., c-1988, page 136.
8) Johansen, Bruce E., Forgotten Founders-How The American Indian Helped Shape Democracy, Roston: The Harvard Common Press, c-1982, pages xv, 74.
9) Bigelow, John, Editor, The Complete Works of Benjamin Franklin, Volume 11, page 210. New York:Grosset 8c Dunlap, c-1867, page
10) Van Doren, Carl, Benjamin Franklin, New York:Viking Press, c-1938, page
11) Porter, C. Fayne, Our Indian Heritage, (chapter: Hiawatha, the Mohawk-Father of Our Constitution.), Philadelphia:Chilton Book Co., c-1964, page 10.
12) Weatherford, Jack McIver, Indian Givers-How The Indians of The Americas Transformed The World, New York:Crown Publishers, Inc., c-1988, page 129.
13) Alden, John R., Pioneer America, New York:Knopf, c-1966, page
14) Editors, Reader's Digest, Through Indian Eyes, c-1995, The Reader's Digest Association, Inc.page 148.
15) Weatherford, Jack McIver, Indian Givers-How The Indians of The Americas Transformed The World, New York:Crown Publishers, Inc., c-1988, page 126.
16) Alden, John R., Pioneer America, New York:Knopf, c-1966, pages 87,& 104.
17) Waldman, Carl, Encyclopedia of Native American Tribes, New York:Facts on File, c-1988.
18) Josephy, Alvin M. Jr., 500 Nations, New York:Alfred A. Knopf, c-1994, page 252.
19) Alden, John R., Pioneer America, New York:Knopf, c-1966, page 88.
20) Hope, A. Guy, & Janet Barker Hope, Symbols of The Nation, Washington, D. C., Public Affairs Press, c-l973, page 294.

'THOMAS JEFFERSON-FATHER OF THE DECLARATION OF INDEPENDENCE'

1) Jefferson, Thomas, Notes on Virginia, Philadelphia:R. T. Rawle, Publishers, c-l801, page
2) Kopper, Philip, Smithsonian Book of North American Indians-Before the Coming of the Europeans, Washington, D. C.:Smithsonian Books, c-1986, page 13.
3) Ibid, page 271.
4) Johansen, Bruce E., Forgotten Founders, Harvard: The Harvard Common Press, c-1982, page xvi.
5) Burt, Jesse, & Ferguson, Robert B., The Indians of The Southeast: Then and Now, Nashville:Abingdon Press, c-1973, page 61.
6) Wright, J. Leitch, Jr., The Only Land They Knew: The Tragic Story of The American Indians in the Old South, New York:Free Press, c-1981, page 220.
6a) Nabokov, Peter, Edited by, Native American Testimony, New York:Penguin Group, c-1978, 1991, page 78.
7) Hudson, Charles, The Southeastern Indians, Knoxville: The University of Tennessee Press, c-1976, page 452.
8) Jefferson, Thomas, Notes on Virginia, Philadelphia:R. T. Rawle, Publishers, c-1801, page
9) Nabokov, Peter, Edited by, Native American Testimony, New York:Penguin Group, c-197S, 1991, page 148.
10) La Farge, Oliver, Pictorial History of The American Indian, New York:Crown Publishers, Inc., c-1956, 1974 by the estate of Oliver La Farge, Alvin M. Josephy, Jr., and Crown Publishers, Inc., page 29.
11) Jefferson, Thomas, Notes on Virginia, Philadelphia: R. T. Rawle, Publishers, c-1801, page
12) Columbia Viking Desk Encyclopedia, New York: The Viking Press, c-1953.

'MISSIONARY SUCCESS STORY AMONG THE CHEROKEE.'

1) National Geographic Society, The World of The American Indian, Washington, D. C., c-1974, 1979, pages 11, 14, 16, 18, 20, 22.
2) Eliot, Charles W., Editor, The Harvard Classics:American Historical Documents, (New York:P. F. Collier & Son, c-1938), page 257.
3) The United States Statutes at Large, Volume 3.
4) Luccock, Halford E., & Hutchinson, Paul, The Story of Methodism, New York & Cincinnati: The Methodist Book Concern, c-1926, pages 60-61.
5) Cannon, James 3rd, History of Southern Methodist Missions, Nashville:Cokesbury Press, c-1926, pages 256-2S7.
6) Noley, Homer, The First White Frost, Nashville:Abingdon Press, c-1991, pages 42-43.
7) Barclay, W. Crawford, Early American Methodism:Missionary Motivation and Expansion, 1796-1844, (New York:Board of Mission and Extension, c-1949. Pages 201-202.
8) Noley, Homer, The First White Frost, Nashville:Abingdan Press, c-1991, page 53.
9) McLoughlin, Wm. G., Cherokees & Missionaries - 1789-1839, pages 75-76, 248.
10) Luccock, Halford E., & Hutchinson, Paul, The Story of Methodism, New York: & Cincinnati: The Methodist Book Concern, c-1926, pages 308-309.
11) Noley, Homer, The First White Frost, Nashville:Abingdon Press, c-l991, pages 89-90.
12) McLoughlin, Wm. G., Cherokees and missionaries-1789-1839, page 164.
13) Lazenby, Marion Elias, History of Methodism in Alabama and West Florida, (Published by the North Alabama Conference, and Alabama-West Florida Conference, 1960), pages 173-174,
14) West, Anson, History of Methodism in Alabama, (Nashville:Publishing House Methodist Episcopal Church South, c-1893, pages 386-388.

15) McLoughlin,Wm. G., Cherokees and Missionaries-1789-1839, page 165.
16) West, Anson, History of Methodism in Alabama, Nashville:Publishing House Methodist Episcopal Church South, c-1893, page
17) Malone, Henry T., Cherokees of The Old South - People in Transition, Athens:University of Ga. Press, c-l956, page 111.
18) McLoughlin Wm. G., Cherokees & Missionaries-1789-1839, page 165.
19) West, Anson, History of Methodism in Alabama, Nashville:Publishing House Methodist Episcopal Church South, c-1893, page 389.
20) Ibid, page
21) Georgia Act of Legislature, Extending Jurisdiction over The Cherokee Nation, 1829.
22) Barclay W. Crawford, Early American Methodism:Missionary Motivation and Expansion, 1796-1844,
N. Y.: Board of Mission and Extension, c-1949, page
10a) Cannon, James 3rd, History of Southern Methodist Missions, Nashville:Cokesbury Press, c-1926, page 263.

'FOR THE BEAUTY OF THE EARTH'

1) Stop and Smell The Roses (words and music by Mac Davis, Screen Gems-Columbia Music Corp. & Doc Severinsen,

'IN SEARCH OF CHAMPIONS'

1) Calligraphy, 'Like a Tree Planted by The Rivers of Water', by Margurite Busby
2) National Geographic Magazine

'THE AMAZING MONARCH'

1) Brewer, Jo, Wings In The Meadow, Boston:Houghton Mifflin Co., c-1967, page xvii.
2) Mann, Tom, Junior Fisherman Magazine, Vol. 1, number 3, Fall, 1983, Shane Ford, "Mother Nature's Gallery, page 33.
3) Brewer, Jo, Wings In The meadow, Boston:Houghton Mifflin Co., c-1967, page 164.
4) Southern Living, "The Miracle of The Monarch:, Oct., 1984, pages 56-57.

'THIS IS A SANCTUARY'

1) Webster Dictionary - The Southwestern Co. Nashville, c-1966.
2) Dr. Roy Wood, slang of The Chattahoochee Valley that he taught me.
3) Editors. The United Methodist Hymnal, Nashville: Abingdon Press, c-1964, 1966, Doxology.
4) Hebrews 8:10-12, 24, 9:2, Isaiah 60:13, Scripture quotations are from the Revised Standard Version of the Bible, copyright 1946, 1952, 1971 by the Division of Christian Education of the National Council of Churches of Christ in the USA. Used by permission. All rights reserved.

'THE OLYMPIC GAMES'

1) Funk and Wagnalls Standard Dictionary; Funk and Wagnalls Co., New York, c-1960.
2) The Book of Knowledge, The Grolier Society, Inc., New York, c-1960, Vol. 3, page 1O28 & Vol. 7, page 2618.
3) Owens, Jesse, with Paul Neimark, Jesse-The Man Who Outran Hitler', c-1978, pages 71, 77

'MY EARTHWORM FRIENDS'

1) National Geographic Society, The World of The American Indian, c-1974, 1979 by The National Geographic Society, Washington, D. C., pages 11, 14, 16, 18, 20, 22.

'SUPER GRAINS CEREAL OF MY DAILY BREAD'

1) Rodale, Robert of Emmaus Gardens, a personal letter, response to questions of research about The American Indian's discovery and use of Amaranth and the hyberdation of The Golden Grain Amaranth of The Aztec Indians.
2) Kamut - Arrowhead Mills, Inc., box 2059, Hereford, Texas 79045 USA c-497. Kamut - Great Grains Exposed - Ancients - from the Past - to the future. Kamut brand wheat is the most buttery, rich, nutty tasting of the grains, delivering optimum nutrition), 20% to 40% more protein that modern wheat}, and it's easily digestible as well. Quinoa goes a long way. Considered the #1 whole protein cereal by The United Nations World Health Organization. Rich and balanced with complete protein, delicious, light and easily digestible. Also referred to as the "Super-Grain". Brown Rice, so important as a food that
3) It's considered synonymous with the word, "meal". Whole Rice kernels are the most wholesome and nutrient dense when compared to other rice.
4) Amaranth, rediscovered Sacred Aztec "Grain of the Future". Averaging over 16% [protein, contains rich source of fiber, calcium, & phosphorus. Appreciated for its wild, woodsy flavor and remarkable vitality and energizing qualities. 3) Amaranth Flakes: Amaranth: an attractive, colorful plant that grows shoulder-high plumes containing

nutrient-dense seeds. The leaves, stem, and flowers display brilliant shades of purple, red, and gold that glow radiantly in the summer sun. The potent little are barely larger that a grain of sand and are produced in massive numbers. Sometimes more than a half-million seeds per plant. Centuries ago, amaranth was a life-sustaining plant for advanced cultures in Mexico, Central, and South America. But in 1521, Hernando Cortez, realizing the importance of amaranth to the Aztecs of Mexico, destroyed their Gelds and stores of amaranth as part of a strategy of total conquest. A staple food of millions virtually disappeared for over 400 years. Today, modern agriculture has revived amaranth, which the National Academy of Sciences views as one of the most promising unexploited food crops in the United States.

Few plants excel amaranth in versatility. When young, the plant produces large, leafy greens that are an excellent source of iron and calcium. Amaranth is one of the few broad-leaf plants that produces significant amounts of edible, nutritious grain. The crop is beneficial to growers in that it resists pest, heat, and drought. All in all, centuries of use verify that amaranth is one of the greatest gifts of Nature to all peoples.

Immortal Amaranth - this ancient food crop of the Americas get its name from the Greek word, "Immortal", which refers to the remarkable durability of amaranth . While some grains like corn and rice can lose their life force in only a few decades, amaranth discovered in ancient Aztec ruins has demonstrated its ability to sprout.

Aztec "Super-Grain" - Why is amaranth called a 'super-grain'? First, because of its superior amino acid profile. It has an excellent balance of the essential acids that the human body cannot manufacture. Lysine and methionine, lacking in most grains, are abundant in amaranth. The total protein content is as high as 20% - higher than all other cereal grains. Compared to most common cereals, the grain has superior phosphorus and iron content. Arrowhead Mills chose amaranth to blend with other nutritious whole grains and star in this truly super-cereal with s naturally sweet, nut-like flavor. The mystical, ancient grain of the Aztecs, Mayans, and Incas may prove to be one of their richest legacies. (Arrowhead mills, Inc.)

4) The Benefits of Flax. Health Valley's Organic Golden Flax Cereal is the first cereal that is high in Omega-3 fatty acids and lignans. Omega-3 fatty acids are a type of "good" fat that is essential to good health. What makes these fats unique is that our bodies cannot manufacture them - we need to get them from food. Unfortunately, studies have shown that most diets do not provide enough of these essential fatty acids. Flax seeds are nature's best plant source of Omega-3 fatty acids, as well as a special type of protective fiber called lignans. In fact, flax seeds contain 20% Omega-3 by weight.

Health Valley is the first company to recognize the nutritional benefits of flax seeds and use them in its cereal. Each serving of our Organic Golden Flax Cereal provides 1,000 milligrams of Omega-3, plus 1,000 mg. Of Omega-6 and 700 mg. Of Omega-9. Health Valley's Organic Golden Flax Cereal not only tastes great, but with Omega-3, lignans, fiber and protein, it is loaded with great nutrition. Health Valley Company, 16100 Foothill Boulevard, Irwindale, California 91706-7811.

'BEHOLD THE POTTER'S WHEEL'

1) National Geographic Society, Editors, The World of The American Indian, Washington, D. C., c-1974, 1979, page 63.
2) Jeremiah 18:1-12, Scripture quotations are from the Revised Standard Version of the Bible, copyright 1946, 1952, 1971 by the Division of Christian Education of the National Council of the Churches of Christ in the USA. Used by permission. All rights reserved.
3) Van Briggle Art Pottery, Colorado Springs, Colorado, brochure.

'HELEN KELLER-FIRST LADY OF COURAGE'

1) Data from leaflets - Helen Keller, and Helen Keller: Worker for the Blind, American Foundation for The Blind, Inc., 15 West 16th., Street, New York, N. Y., 10011, (Courtesy of Ivy Green, Tuscumbia,Alabama.
2) Helen Keller, The Story of My Life, Dell Publishing Company. Inc., 750 Third Avenue, New York, N.Y., c- 1902, by Helen Keller, c-1954, Doubleday and Company, Inc., c-1961 by Eleanor Roosevelt, Dell, page 31.
3) Ibid, page 32.
4) Ibid, page 34.
5) Data from The Miracle Worker brochure, (Courtesy of Ivy Green, Tuscumbia, Alabama.).
6) Same a 2 above, page 117.

'EAGLES'

1) Isaiah 40:31, Scripture quotations are from the Revised Standard Version of the Bible, copyright 1946, 1952, 1971 by the Division of Christian Education of the National Council of the Churches of Christ in the USA. Used by permission. All rights reserved.
2) Webster's Dictionary, The World Publishing Co, Cleveland, Ohio and New York, Volume 1, page 528, c-1940.
3) Smith s Bible Dictionary, Philadelphia:A. J. Holmes Co., page 82.
4) Psalms 103:5, (same as 1 above).
5) Webster s Universal Dictionary of The English Language, being the Unabridged Dictionary by Noah Webster, L.L.D., Volume 2, The World Publishing Co., Cleveland, Ohio, & New York, c-1940.
6) Carter, President Jimmy, Sources of Strength, New York: Times Books, c-1997, pages 167-169.
6a) Wright, J. Leitch, Jr., The Only Land The Knew, New York: The Free Press, c-1981, page 19.

6b) Hudson, Charles, The Southeastern Indians, Knoxville: The University of Tennessee Press, c-1976, page 163.
7) Cherokee Historical Association and Museum, Cherokee, North Carolina.
8) Views from a Sacred Mountain by Jon Magnuson. Copyright 1984 by Christian Acentury Foundation. Reprinted by permission from the August 1-8, 1984 issue of The Christian Century.
9) National Archives - -pictures of Symbols of Eagles holding 6 arrows for The Iroquois Confederacy, and an Eagle holding 13 arrows far The 13 Colonies A, The USA.
10) Isaiah 40:31, Scripture quotations are from (same as 1 above).

'LEGEND OF BEAR-MEAT CABIN'

1) West, Anson, History of Methodism in Alabama, Nashville: Publishing House Methodist Episcopal Church South, -1893, page 120.
2) Ibid, page 120-121.
3) Ibid, page 121.
4) Ibid, page 125.

'AMERICA'

1) Great Concepts —
2) Lincoln, President Abraham, The Gettysburg Address, Booklet of The National Park Service, Washington, D. C.
3) Bates, Katharine Lee, "America", National Archives, Washington, D. C.
4) Wilson, President Woodrow, from a speech, "Challenge to The Nation" and notes on The League of Nations.
5) Carter, President Jimmy, from a speech.
6) Lincoln, Abraham, end of The Gettysburg Address.
7) Pledge of Allegiance of The United States of America.

'GEORGE WASHINGTON - FATHER OF AMERICA'

1) Thomas, Lowell, The Vital Spark, Doubleday and Co., Inc., Garden City, N.Y., c-1959, pages 356- 359.
2) Jones, Robert F., George Washington, Twayne Publishers, G. K. Hall and Co., c-1979, pages 40-41.
3) Flexner, James Thomas, George Washington In The American Revolution 1775-1783, Boston & Toronto:Little, Brown, and Co., c-1967, 1968, pages 9-10, 252.
4) Jones, Robert F., George Washington, Boston: Twayne Publisher, G. K. Hall and Co., c-1979, page 161.
5) Flexner, James Thomas, George Washington In The American Revolution 1775-1783, Boston & Toronto:Little, Brown, and Co., c-1967, 1968, page
6) Thomas, Lowell, The Vital Spark, Garden City, N. Y.:Doubleday and Co., Inc., c-1959, page 359.

'ABRAHAM LINCOLN'

10 Foote, Anna Elizabeth, and Skinner, Avery Warner, Makers and Defenders of America, c-1910, pages 231-233.
2) Ibid, page 236.
3) Thomas, Lowell, The Vital Spark, Doubleday and Co., Inc., Garden City, N. Y., c-1959, page 444.
4) The Grolier Society, Inc., The Book of Knowledge, New York, c-1960, Volume 5, page 1649.
5) Thomas, Lowell, The Vital Spark, Doubleday and Co., Inc., Garden City, N. Y., c-1959, page 444.
6) Foote, Anna Elizabeth, and Skinner, Avery Warner, Makers and Defenders of America, c-1910, page 238.
7) Noll, Mark, article - "The perplexing Faith of Abraham Lincoln", in Christianity Today, February 15, 1985, pages 12-16.
8) Thomas, Lowell, The Vital Spark, Doubleday and Co., c-1959, page 447.
9) Abraham Lincoln - From His Own Words and Contemporary Accounts, edited by Roy Edgar Appleman, National Park Service, Washington, D. C., 1942.

'NATIVE AMERICAN AWARENESS-THE RICHNESS OF AMERICAN IN HER INDIAN HERITAGE'

1) Acts 10:17-23, A Romans 1:8-14, Scripture quotations are from the Revised Standard Version of the Bible, copyright 1946, 1952, 1971 by the Division of Christian Education of the National Council of the Churches of Christ in the USA. Used by permission. All rights reserved.
2) Webster's Dictionary - Awareness - The Southwestern Co., c-1966.
3) Letter &from The United States Department of Agriculture.
4) Porter, C. Fayne, Our Indian Heritage-Profiles of 12 Great Leaders, Philadelphia:Chilton Book Co., c-l964, page 3.
5) National Geographic Society, official Journal of The National Geographic Society, Washington, D. C., October, 1991, page 82.
6) National Geographic Society, Editors, The World of The American Indian, Washington, D. C., c-1974, 1979, pages 11, 14, 16, 18, 20, 22.
7) Adair, James, History of The American Indian, New York:Promontory Press, c-1930, pages xxix, 20, 38, 50.
8) Johansen, Bruce E., Forgotten Founders, Harvard & Boston: The Harvard Common Press, c-1982, pages 102-103.
9) Editors, The Smithsonian Magazine, Washington, D. C., Smithsonian Museum, page

'JESUS IS THE BREAD OF LIFE'

1) John 6:31-35,& 51; 1 Corinthians 10:16-17, Scripture quotations are from the Revised Standard Version of the Bible, copyright 1946, 1952, 1971 by the Division of Christian Education of the National Council of Churches of Christ in the USA. Used by permission. All rights reserved.
la) The Grolier Society, Inc., The Book of Knowledge, Danbury, Ct.,c-1991, Volume 4, page 385.
2) The Encyclopedia Americana, New York:Americana Corp. c-1951, Volume 4, page 447.
3) Corson, Sarah, SIFAT, Servants in Faith and Technology, Wedowee, Al.
4) O'Neil, E. S., Mother Earth News.
4a) The Interpreter's Dictionary of The Bible, Nashville: Abingdon Press, c-1962, page 463.
5) Matthew's 6:11, Scripture quotations are from the Revised Standard Version of the Bible, copyright 1946, 1952, 1971 by the Division of Christian Education of the National Council of the Churches of Christ in the USA. Used by permission. All rights reserved.
6) Cruden's Concordance, Philadelphia: The John C. Winston Co., c-1949.
7) Webster's New World Dictionary and Student Handbook, Nashville: The Southwestern Co., c-1969.
8) The Book of Knowledge, Danbury, Ct.:Grolier, Inc., c-1991, Volume b, page 385.
9) The Encyclopedia Britannica, Volume 2, page 490.
10) Exodus the 16th., chapter, (credit same as 1 above.}.
11) John 6:50, 58, (credit same as 1 above.).
12) Owens, Jesse, Jesse, a Spiritual Autobiography, Plainfield, N. J.: Logos International, c-1978, page
13) John 6:35, 48, 50, 58, Scripture quotations are from the Revised Standard Version of the Bible, copyright 1946, 1952, 1971 by the Division of Christian Education of the National Council of theChurches of Christ in the USA. Used by permission. All rights reserved.
4b) Reader's Digest, February, 1983, page 150, "Our Daily Bread" by Jack Denton Scott.

'WE STAND TODAY ON HOLY GROUND'

1) Exodus 3:1-6, Acts 7:31-34, 1 Peter 2:1-10, Scripture quotations are from the Revised Standard Version of the Bible, copyright 1946, 1952, 1971 by the Division of Christian Education of the National Council of the Churches of Christ in the USA. Used by permission. All rights reserved.
2) Pitts, Dr. Wm. S., Hymn - "The Church in The Wildwood", Cokesbury Hymnal, Nashville: Abingdon Press, page 121.
3) John 8:11, (credit same as 1 above.).
4) Isaiah 40:31, (credit same as 1 above.).
5) The United Methodist Discipline, Nashville: Abingdon Press.
6) 1st, Peter 2:9, (credit same as 1 above.).
7) Wesley, Charles, The United Methodist Hymnal, Nashville: Abingdon Press, c-1986, page 150, "A Charge to keep I Have", based on Leviticus 8:35.

'OUR GOD IS ABLE!'

1) Ephesians 3:14-21, Jude 1:24-25, Scripture quotations are from the Revised Standard Version of the Bible, copyright 1946, 1952, 1971 by the Division of Christian Education of the National Council of Churches of Christ in the USA. Used by permission. All rights reserved.
2) Acts 10:26, (credit same as 1 above.).
3) Romans 3:23, (credit same as 1 above.}.
4) Camp Songs, Methodist Publishing House, Spiritual - "Gonna Sing When The Spirit Says Sing".
5) Mark 8:33, (credit same as 1 above.).
6) Romans 7:24, (credit same as 1 above.).
7) Hebrews 2:18, (credit same as 1 above.).
7a) Ferguson, John L., Our God Is Able, Men's Club, Belmont Methodist Church, Nashville, Tn., c-1951, page 17.
8) 2nd, Timothy 1:12, (credit same as 1 above.).
9) Psalms 23 (credit same as 1 above.).
10) Jude 1:24, (credit same as 1 above.).

'LIVE IN HARMONY!'

1) Coca Cola Jingle - 'Teach The World to Sing in Perfect Harmony', words and music belongs to Shada Music Co. and ?

Index

INDEX OF SAYINGS-PHRASES-AND TERMS.

BIBLIOGRAPHY for *STORIES I LOVE TO TELL.*

Adair, James, History of the American Indian.
Alden, John R., Pioneer America.
Appleman, Roy Edgar, Edited by; Abraham Lincoln-From his own Words and Contemporary Accounts.
Barclay, William, Early American Methodist:Missionary Motivation & Expansion.
Bible
Bigelow, John, Editor, The Complete Works of Benjamin Franklin.
Brown & Edwards, Cherokee and Proud of it.
Cannon, James, 3rd., History of Southern Methodist Missions.
Carter, President Jimmy, Sources of Strength.
Colden, Cadwallader, The History of The Five Nations.
Cohen, Felix S., article "Americanizing The White Man", American Scholar.
Cochran, Thomas C., Pennsylvania.
Curtis, Will, That's The Nature of Things.
Deur, Lynn, Indian Chief.
Dudley, Joseph 'Iron Eye'-Choteau Creek.
Editors-The Grolier Society, Inc.-The Book of Knowledge.
Editors-National Geographic Society-The World of The American Indian.
Editors-The United States at Large Statutes-Volume 3.
Editors-Smithsonian-Native Peoples Magazine.
Editors-Reader's Digest-America's Fascinating Indian Heritage.
Editors-Smithsonian-North American Indian-Before the Coming of The Europeans.
Editors-Reader's Digest -Through Indian Eyes.
Editor-The Book of Knowledge.
Fleming, Alden O., Manabozho-The Indian's Story of Hiawatha.
Flexner, James Thomas, George Washington in The American Revolution.
Foote, Anna Elizabeth, & Skinner, Avery Warner—Makers and Defender of America.
Foreman, Grant, The Five Civilized Tribes.
Hendrickson, Robert, The Encyclopedia of Word and Phrase Origins.
Holt, Alfred H., Phrase Origins-A Study of Familiar Expressions.
Hope, A. Guy, Janet Barker Hope, Symbols of The Nation.

Johansen, Bruce E., Forgottten Founders-How The American Indian Helped Shape Democracy.
Josephy, Alvin M. Jr., The Indian Heritage of America.
Josephy, Alvin M. Jr., 500 Nations.
Josephy, Alvin M. Jr., The Patriot Chiefs.
Jones, Robert F., George Washington.
Koch, Adriene, Editor- The American Enlightenment.
LaFarge, Oliver, A Pictorial History of the American Indian.
Lawson, John, History of Carolina.
Lazenby, M. E., History of Methodism in Al. And West Florida.
Longfellow, Henry Wadsworth, The Legend of Hiawatha.
Malone, Henry Thompson, Cherokees of The Old South.
Luccock, Halford E. & Hutchinson, Paul, The Story of Methodism.
Magnuson, Jon, The Christian Century-Views from a Sacred Mounttain.
Marquis, Arnold, A Guide to America's Indians.
McDonald, William Lindsey, The Old North Field.
McDonald, William 'Bill' Lindsey, Lore of The River.
McLoughlin, Wm. G., Cherokees & Missionaries-1789-1839.
McNickle, D'Arcy, They Came Here First.
McTyeire, Holland N., A History of Methodism.
Mooney, James, Historical Sketch of The Cherokee.
Mooney, James, Myths of The Cherokee.
Morgan, Henry Lewis , Ancient Society.
Noley, Homer, The First White Frost.
Noll, Mark, Christianity Today- "The Perplexing Faith of Abraham Lincoln".
Owens, Jesse, Jesse.
Owen, Marie, Our State-Alabama.
O'Donnell, James H. 3rd., Southern Indians in The American Revolution.
Payne, John Howard, Journal of Cherokee Studies.
Peare, Catherine Owens, William Penn, a Biography.
Pickett, Albert James, History of Alabama.
Phillips, John Franklin, The American Indian in Alabama and The Southeast.
Phillips, John Franklin, The Indian Heritage of Americans.
Phillips, John Franklin, Chief Junaluska of The Cherokee Indian Nation.
Porter, C. Fayne, Our Indian Heritage.
Schoolcraft, Henry R., History of The Indian Tribes of North America.
Smith's Bible Dictionary.

Staples, Thomas S., Jesse H. Amers, Merlin M. Ames-My America.
Thomas, Lowell, The Vital Spark.

Swanton, John R., The Indian Tribes of North America.
Viole, Herman J. After Columbus-The Smithsonian Chronicle of The North American Indians
Waldman, Carl, Encyclopedia of Native American Tribes.
Wallace, Paul A W., Pennsylvania-Seed of a Nation.
Wallace, Paul A. W., The White Roots of Peace.
Weatherford, Jack McIver, Indian Givers.
Weatherford, Jack McIveer, Native Roots-How The Indian Enriched America.
Walker, Ricky 'Butch', Warrior Mountain Folklore.
West, Anson, History of Methodism in Alabama.
Webster's Dictionary.

Acknowledgements:

The Author gratefully acknowledges the influence of many stories and books that he read across the past 25 years, and more, in the evolvement of these stories. Many of these stories were told to the children in the churches the author was serving across the past 50 years. Many of the stories were told to Boy Scout, Girl Scout, Brownies, Cubs, and many other groups and clubs. Many of them were told to classes in schools-kindergarten up to college and university classes. On a volunteer basis, the author has told these stories in several hundred settings, with much joy and satisfaction, and sometimes breakfast, lunch, or dinner or refreshments, and a couple of times, the day's expenses.

Bibliography in my personal library.

American Indians, James Adair.
American Epic, The Story of The American Indian, Marriott & Rachlin.
Amaranth from the past for the Future, John N. Cole.
American Lands and Peoples, J. Russell Smith.
Archeological Salvage in The Walter F. George Basin of The Chattahoochee River in Alabama, David L. DeJarnette.
Brother Eagle, Sister Sky
Appalachian Wilderness, Eliot Porter.
Cherokee and Proud of It, Brenda K. Brown, & Marcella S. Edwards.
Cherokee Roots 1 & 2, Bob Blankenship.
Chief Junaluska of The Cherokee Indian Nation, John Franklin Phillips.
Choteau Creek-a Sioux Reminiscence, Joseph 'Iron Eye' Dudley.
Fireside Book of North American Indian Folktales, Allan & Paulette MacFarlan.
500 Nations, Alvin M. Josephy, Jr.
Forgotten Founders, Bruce E. Johansen.
First White Frost, Homer Noley.
Handbook of American Indian Games, Allan & Paulette MacFarlan.
History of Alabama, Albert James Pickett.
Historical Sketch of The Cherokee , James Mooney
Indian Arts, Andrew Hunter Whiteford.
Indians of The Southeast: Then and Now, Burt & Ferguson.
Indian Crafts and Lore.
Living Faith, Jimmy Carter.
Last of The Mahicans, James Fenimore Cooper.
Legends of The American Indians, Henry Rowe Schoolcraft.
Myths of The Cherokee, James Mooney.
Native American Wisdom, Running Press.
Native American Testimony, Edited by Peter Nabokov.
Pictorial History of The American Indian, Oliver LaFarge.
North American Indians, Norman Brancroft-Hunt.
Screaming Hawk, Patton Boyle.
Shaman Daughter, Nan F. Salerno and Rosamond M. Vanderburgh.
Sources of Strength, President Jimmy Carter.
The Lore of The River-The Shoals of Long Ago, William Lindsey McDonald.
The Old North Field, William Lindsey McDonald.
The Navajo Code Talkers, Doria A. Paul.
The History of Etowah County,
Touch The Earth, compiled by T.C. McLuhan.
The World of The American Indian, National Geographic Society.
The North American Indians, Brancroft-Hunt.
Through Indian Eyes, Reader's Digest.
Smithsonian Book of North American Indians.
Trail of Tears, John Ehle.
The Cherokee Indian Nation, edited by Duane H. King.
The Southeastern Indians, Charles Hudson.
The Death and Rebirth of The Seneca, Anthony F. C. Wallace.
The Indian Heritage of Americans, John Franklin Phillips
The American Indian in Alabama and The Southeast, John Franklin Phillips.
The Iroquois Book of Life-White Roots of Peace, Paul Wallace.
The Indian Tribes of North America, James R. Swanton.
The Lumbee Methodists, Smith.
The Story of The Trail of Tears, R. Conrad Stein.
The George Catlin Book of American Indians, Royal B. Hassrick.
Voices, Native American hymns and Worship Resources.
Warrior Mountain Folklore, Rickey 'Butch' Walker.
Windows of The Past, Florence C. Lister and Lynn Wilson.
Woodward Reminiscences of The Creek and Muscogee Indians, Thomas S. Woodward.